Discovering Algebra
An Investigative Approach

D1410955

Calculator Notes for the
Texas Instruments TI-83 and TI-83/84 Plus

DISCOVERING

MATHEMATICS™

Key Curriculum Press
Innovators in Mathematics Education

Teacher's Materials Project Editor: Elizabeth DeCarli

Editor: Josephine Noah

Editorial Assistant: Aaron Madrigal

Writers: Eric Kamischke, David Rasmussen

Project Manager: Rozi Harris, Interactive Composition Corporation

Copyeditor: David Abel

Editorial Production Supervisor: Christine Osborne

Production Director: McKinley Williams

Production Coordinator: Ann Rothenbuhler

Text Designer: Jenny Somerville

Art Editor: Jason Luz

Composition, Technical Art, Prepress: Interactive Composition Corporation

Cover Designers: Jill Kongabel, Marilyn Perry

Printer: Data Reproductions

Textbook Product Manager: James Ryan

Executive Editor: Casey FitzSimons

Publisher: Steven Rasmussen

© 2007 by Key Curriculum Press. All rights reserved.

Cover Photo Credits: Background image: Pat O'Hara/DRK Photo. Boat image: Marc Epstein/DRK Photo. All other images: Ken Karp Photography.

Limited Reproduction Permission

The publisher grants the teacher who purchases *Discovering Algebra: An Investigative Approach, Calculator Notes for the Texas Instruments TI-83 and TI-83/84 Plus* the right to reproduce material for use in his or her own classroom. Unauthorized copying of *Discovering Algebra: An Investigative Approach, Calculator Notes for the Texas Instruments TI-83 and TI-83/84 Plus* constitutes copyright infringement and is a violation of federal law.

®Key Curriculum Press is a registered trademark of Key Curriculum Press. All registered trademarks and trademarks in this book are the property of their respective holders.

Key Curriculum Press
1150 65th Street
Emeryville, CA 94608
(510) 595-7000
editorial@keypress.com
www.keypress.com

Printed in the United States of America
10 9 8 7 6 5 4 3   11 10 09 08   ISBN 978-1-55953-773-5

Contents

Introduction

One of the challenges of publishing an innovative textbook like *Discovering Algebra: An Investigative Approach* is finding a way to effectively incorporate rapidly changing technology. To accommodate students with different—and ever-changing—types of graphing calculators, we have addressed this challenge by referring to calculators in the student text generically and by providing detailed notes for several different types of calculators in separate books and on the Internet, at www.keymath.com/DA. As new calculator technology is introduced, Key Curriculum Press will create new calculator notes to accommodate the changing technology.

This book gives students specific keystroke instructions for the Texas Instruments TI-83, TI-83 Plus, and TI-84 Plus (including Silver Edition) graphing calculators. Most notes are the same for all three calculators. For the notes that are different, keystrokes for the TI-83 follow those for the TI-83 Plus and TI-84 Plus. Some notes help students use motion sensors, such as the Texas Instruments Calculator-Based Ranger (CBR or CBR 2), to collect data with their calculators. Other notes contain programs for specific investigations or exercises. Among the programs are a few interactive games that give students engaging mathematics experiences. There are a few notes that describe how to use Calculator Software Applications (Apps) available from Texas Instruments. These notes are named, for example, Note 1I/App. Some Apps come preloaded on the TI-83 Plus and TI-84 Plus. (Apps cannot be used on the TI-83.) Others are available for download at the Texas Instruments website, education.ti.com.

Your students will find references to the calculator notes throughout the student text. For example, on page 203, you will find a reference that says: [▶ See **Calculator Note 3D** to learn how to use the LINES program. ◀] This reference indicates that in Calculator Note 3D there is a calculator program and there are instructions on how to use the program. All calculator notes for each lesson are mentioned in the materials list of the *Discovering Algebra Teacher's Edition*. How much your students need these notes will depend on their experience with graphing calculators and with the particular graphing calculator methods you choose to use to explore concepts in *Discovering Algebra*. The notes will be particularly useful if your students use many different types of calculators.

You may want to copy and distribute the notes as they are needed, or you can copy and distribute all of the notes for each chapter as you begin work on that chapter. If your students have had limited experience with graphing calculators, a good strategy is to distribute a copy of the notes to each student and encourage students to keep the notes in a special section of their notebooks. Another strategy would be to make enough copies for each group of students to have access to one or two copies of the notes, stored either in three-hole report covers or individually in hanging files. If your students have had a lot of experience with graphing calculators, however, you may need only one or two copies of the notes for classroom reference. If your students use many different calculator brands and models, you'll need to make copies of the notes for each type of calculator. If students need home access to a note, they can download all the notes from the *Discovering Algebra* website, www.keymath.com/DA.

Even if you don't usually copy a complete set of calculator notes for each student, you may find it helpful to distribute copies to all students for particular sections of material. For example, many of the sections in the student text contain special calculator programs. If students input these programs rather than link them, they will need access to a hard copy of the program. For shorter programs you can display the program commands on an overhead display, but if students are using a variety of calculators, you'll probably be better off providing each student with notes for his or her particular calculator. If you have TI Connect™ linking software and access to a computer, you can take advantage of the programs and data stored on the *Calculator Programs and Data CD* or *Teaching Resources CD* available with the Teaching Resources or on the web at www.keymath.com/DA. You can download programs or data from the CDs or Internet to a computer and then to a calculator linked to the computer. Students can link their calculators to transfer the data and programs.

You will also find it useful to make available to students a copy of the *TI-83 Graphing Calculator Guidebook, TI-83 Plus Graphing Calculator Guidebook,* or *TI-84 Plus Graphing Calculator Guidebook.* In addition, Texas Instruments can provide you with a transparency of the calculator or a classroom poster that can help you or students explain to others a sequence of keystrokes. Overhead graphing calculators are also helpful in demonstrating calculator procedures. Additionally, you might wish to use TI-SmartView™ emulator software, which allows you to project an image of the calculator and its display as you press keys and enter commands.

The TI-83/84 Plus Data App

The *Calculator Programs and Data CD, Teaching Resources CD,* and website also contain the data sets for the TI-83 Plus and TI-84 Plus stored as an application. This application will allow you to store all of the necessary data sets for *Discovering Algebra* on your calculator where they will not take up RAM. Follow the instructions in the TI Connect software to download the Application DiscAlg.8xk into your calculator. To access lists stored in the application, press the APPS key. Highlight :DISCALG and press ENTER ENTER. Select the chapter. Scroll and press ENTER to select each list you want to use. Scroll right to highlight Load and select 2:Load. You will see a message that the lists have been loaded into the List Editor. If an error message appears, a list with the same name is probably already in the List Editor. You can now select more lists to load or Quit the application.

Alternative Data Collection Programs

For each calculator note that requires the use of a CBR, the instructions in this book describe how to use the EasyData App or a particular program. An alternative approach is to use the CBRSET and CBRGET programs. The CBRSET program allows you, the teacher, the set up each CBR in advance. To do this, connect each CBR to your calculator and run CBRSET. At the prompts, enter the total time in seconds, S, and the total number of samples, N. Now, students do not need to connect the CBR to a calculator before collecting data. They simply press the trigger. After collecting data, students connect the CBR to a calculator and run CBRGET. The CBRGET program transfers time and distance data into lists L1 and L2, and then displays a scatter plot.

```
PROGRAM:CBRSET
Prompt S,N
round(S/N,5)→I
If I>0.2:-0.25int(-4I)→I
Send({0})
Send({1,11,2,0,0,0})
Send({3,I,N,1,0,0,0,0,1,1})
```

```
PROGRAM:CBRGET
Send({5,1})
Get(L₂)
Get(L₁)
Plot1(Scatter,L₁,L₂,·)
ZoomStat
```

Note 0A • Fractions

Your calculator will convert a decimal number to a fraction. Enter the decimal number and press MATH 1 (▸Frac) ENTER. This is the "convert to fraction" command. If the number is a repeating decimal number, be sure to enter about fifteen digits of the pattern. If the calculator can't find a fraction with a denominator of less than five digits, it will display your original decimal number.

```
MATH NUM CPX PRB       .0625▸Frac           .0018▸Frac
1:▸Frac                           1/16                9/5000
2:▸Dec                 .272727272727▸Fr     .001▸Frac
3:³                    ac                                  .001
4:³√(                             3/11      .001001001001▸Fr
5:×√                   π▸Frac               ac
6:fMin(                    3.141592654                1/999
7↓fMax(
```

The division sign and the fraction bar are the same key on this calculator. The key shows ÷; the screen shows /. To work with simple fractions like $\frac{4}{7}$ and improper fractions like $\frac{7}{4}$, simply enter them into your calculator using the ÷ key. To see the answer displayed as a fraction, you must use the "convert to fraction" command from the math menu.

The calculator will reduce, add, subtract, multiply, and divide fractions. Often you don't need to use parentheses around a fraction, but when in doubt, put in the parentheses.

```
15/18▸Frac             2/3*3/5▸Frac         2/3+3/5*4/7-1/2▸      (11+4/7)+(5+5/14
            5/6                     2/5      Frac                 )▸Frac
2/3+3/5▸Frac           (2/3)/(3/5)▸Frac               107/210               237/14
         19/15
2/3-3/5▸Frac                        10/9
          1/15        (2/3)²▸Frac
                                     4/9
```

Working with Mixed Numbers

When working with mixed numbers like $11\frac{4}{7}$, you must insert an addition sign between the whole number and the fraction.

To convert an improper fraction to a mixed number, first subtract the whole-number part of the decimal number, then enter the "convert to fraction" command.

```
237/14
        16.92857143
Ans-16▸Frac
               13/14
16+13/14
        16.92857143
```

Note 0B • Exponents

There are several ways to raise a number to a power by using the calculator. The simplest way to square a number (raise it to the second power) is to use the x² key. Enter the number you want to square and then press x². When you press ENTER, the calculator will multiply the number by itself. You can calculate x^3 by

(continued)

entering a number and then pressing [MATH] [3] [ENTER]. For all powers (including the second and third powers if you wish), you can use the [^] key.

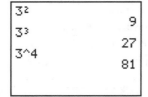

Order of operations requires that you do all operations within parentheses first, evaluate all powers second, multiply and divide from left to right third, and add and subtract from left to right last.

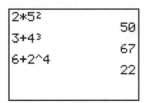

Note 0C • Negation and Subtraction

Negation and subtraction are each performed with a different key on this calculator. Negation, the [(–)] key, changes the sign of a number or a variable. It is slightly higher and shorter than the subtraction symbol. If you enter the wrong symbol, you will either get an error message, or you will get an unexpected result.

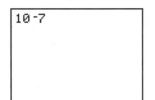

In the order of operations, negation is treated like "multiply by negative one," so it is performed before addition and subtraction but after evaluation of powers. Sometimes you may need to use parentheses to get the correct result.

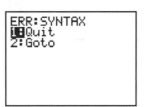

Note 0D • Recursion

The ANS command on the calculator will allow you to use the result of your last calculation in your next calculation. If you press [ENTER] without pressing another key, the calculator will repeat the last operation on the previous result.

(continued)

Combining these two features allows you to perform on-screen recursion, calculating a new number by repeating the operation using the result of the previous calculation. You can create patterns of numbers (sequences) using the following procedure:

    a. Enter the starting number of your sequence and press ENTER.

    b. Enter an expression using Ans. You can get Ans by pressing any of the operation keys, such as +, −, ×, ÷, ∧, x², or by pressing 2nd [ANS].

    c. Press ENTER ENTER ENTER and so on. Each time you press ENTER, you will get one more term in the sequence.

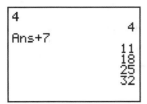 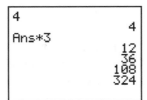 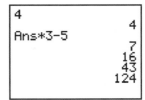

Note 0E • The Chaos Game

To play the Chaos game, follow these steps:

    a. Link or manually enter the program into your calculator. (See **Note 0F** and **Note 0G**.).

    b. Press PRGM and make sure the word EXEC is highlighted. Find the program labeled CHAOS. Press its number or use the down arrow to select the program and press ENTER. To execute the program press ENTER again.

    c. You are asked to choose a Chaos shape. Press the appropriate number or arrow down and press ENTER to select the shape.

    d. You are then asked to enter a fraction between 0 and 1. You can enter this value either as a fraction or a decimal number. Press ENTER.

    e. The calculator will plot 1000 points by following the Chaos rules to plot a fractal. When the program is done, press ENTER.

    f. Follow the directions to replay or to quit.

 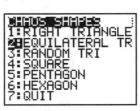 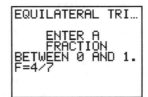 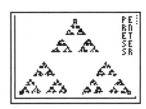

(continued)

```
PROGRAM:CHAOS
ClrHome
Menu("CHAOS SHAPES","RIGHT
   TRIANGLE",1,"EQUILATERAL
   TR",2,"RANDOM    TRI",3,
   "SQUARE",4,"PENTAGON",5,"HEXAGON",
   6,"QUIT",8)
Lbl 1
Disp "  RIGHT TRIANGLE"
{.05,.95,.05}→L₁
{.05,.05,.65}→L₂
Goto 7
Lbl 2
Disp "EQUILATERAL TRIANGLE"
{.05,.95,.5}→L₁
{.05,.05,.65}→L₂
Goto 7
Lbl 3
Disp "RANDOM TRIANGLE"
{rand ,rand ,rand }→L₁
.7{rand ,rand ,rand }→L₂
Goto 7
Lbl 4
Disp "        SQUARE"
{.2,.8,.8,.2}→L₁
{.05,.05,.65,.65}→L₂
Goto 7
Lbl 5
Disp "   PENTAGON"
.5+.35sin(({0,1,2,3,4}72°)→L₁
.35+.35cos(({0,1,2,3,4}72°)→L₂
Goto 7
Lbl 6
```

```
Disp "   HEXAGON"
.5+.35sin(({0,1,2,3,4,5}60°)→L₁
.35+.35cos(({0,1,2,3,4,5}60°)→L₂
Lbl 7
ClrDraw:FnOff
PlotsOff
0→Xmin:1→Xmax
0→Ymin:.7→Ymax
Plot1(Scatter,L₁,L₂,□)
L₂(1)→X:L₂(1)→Y
dim((L₁)→N
Disp "",""    ENTER  A"
Disp "   FRACTION"
Disp "BETWEEN 0 AND 1."
Input "F=",F
For(J,1,1000)
(int(Nrand+1)→P
X+(L₁(P)-X)F→X
Y+(L₂(P)-Y)F→Y
Pt-On(X,Y)
End
Text(0,84,"P  E")
Text(6,84,"R  N")
Text(12,84,"E  T")
Text(18,84,"S  E")
Text(24,84,"S  R")
Pause
Lbl 8
PlotsOff
Disp "  PRESS ENTER",
   "TO REPLAY","","
   PRESS"," 1 AND ENTER",
   "TO QUIT"
```

Note 0F • Linking Programs or Lists

To transfer a program or list from one calculator to another, follow these steps:

   a. Connect two calculators using a link cable. Be sure that the connection is tight on each unit.

   b. Turn on both calculators and on each one press 2nd [LINK].

   c. On the **receiving calculator,** arrow to the right to RECEIVE and press ENTER so that the calculator displays Waiting....

   d. On the **sending calculator,** select 2:All–.... To link a program, arrow down to the name of the program you want to send. To link data, arrow down to the list you want to send.

   e. Press ENTER to select a program or list. (You can select more than one program and/or list and send them simultaneously. Just continue to arrow down and press ENTER at each program or list you want to transfer.) Then arrow right to TRANSMIT and press ENTER.

(continued)

f. When the transfer is complete the name of the program or list transferred will show on the screens of both the sending and receiving calculators.

Errors

If you get Error in Xmit, check that the link cable is pushed all the way into each calculator and try again. Remember that after you arrow to the program or list you want to send, you must press ENTER to select it before you arrow to TRANSMIT. The receiving calculator must show Waiting... before the sending calculator transmits. If the receiving calculator already has a program or list by the same name as the one you are sending, the receiving calculator will show a DuplicateName menu. Select 1:Rename or 2:Overwrite from this menu. If you choose to rename, you must enter a new program name. (See **Note 0G, step b.**)

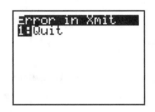

Note 0G • Entering a Program

Your calculator is like a small computer. You can instruct (or program) it to do calculations or to communicate with other devices. What follows are not instructions on how to write a program—they are instructions on how to enter into your calculator a program that has already been written. You must be very careful to enter the commands exactly as they are written. Changing the program in any way will alter how it runs or may cause an error.

There are three ways to enter a program into your calculator. Two easy ways are to download the program from either a computer or another calculator. To use a computer, download the program from a CD-ROM or website directly into your calculator by using TI Connect™ software. You will need the proper cable to link your computer to your calculator. To use another calculator that has the program in its memory, link the two calculators with a link cable and transfer the program. (See **Note 0F.**) The third way is to enter a program manually by following the steps below:

a. Press PRGM and arrow to NEW.

(continued)

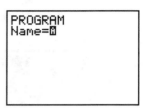

b. Press ENTER and enter the name of the program. You are already in Alpha-Lock so do not press ALPHA unless you want to enter a number into the program's name.

c. Enter the program exactly as you see it. Lowercase letters in the commands of the program indicate that you must find this command on the calculator. You can find many programming commands by pressing PRGM and looking under CTL and I/O. To find other commands, functions, and symbols, either look in the menu of the appropriate calculator key, or press 2nd [CATALOG] and enter the letter that begins the command you want. (You are in still in alpha mode so don't press ALPHA.) Then arrow to the command and press ENTER.

If you enter a command from the calculator keypad using ALPHA characters, the letters will all be uppercase. The command won't look the same as how it's been written and it won't work.

d. Use 2nd [INS] ENTER to insert a new line between two lines. Use DEL on a blank line to delete that line.

e. Press 2nd [QUIT] when you finish entering the program.

Errors

You can edit the program if there is an error or if you need to make a change.

a. Press PRGM and arrow to EDIT. Arrow down to the program and press ENTER.

b. Scroll down through the program to find the error. Studying the entire program on paper is often easier than working from the calculator screen where you can only see a small portion at one time. Use 2nd [INS] or DEL as needed to make changes. Press 2nd [QUIT] when finished.

c. If, when you execute a program, you get an error message that has a Goto option, choose this option. The calculator will automatically switch to EDIT mode and scroll to the line with the error. Then proceed as in **step c.**

Note 0H • Generating Random Integers

You can generate random integers within an interval using the randInt command. Press MATH, arrow to PRB, and select 5:randInt(to access the randInt command.

To randomly generate integers between 1 and 3 inclusive, enter randInt(1,3). Pressing ENTER will generate as many of these integers as you like.

To randomly generate a particular number of integers in an interval, for example, four integers between 1 and 3, enter randInt(1,3,4).

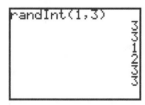
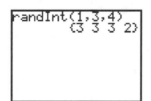

Note 1A • Setting the Mode

Press MODE to display a screen like that shown here. The settings highlighted are the ones that you will use most often in this course. If your calculator does not display these settings, follow the steps below to change them.

1. Use the arrow keys to highlight the setting you want to choose.

2. Press ENTER to register your selection.

3. When you have selected the settings you want, press 2nd [QUIT] to exit from the mode screen.

In this class you will need to change some of these settings during the year. The comments below may not mean much to you now, but your textbook will refer you back to this note several times during the course.

a. NORMAL and SCIentific refer to the way in which numbers are displayed. Both modes are used in the chapter on exponents. Usually this setting should be on NORMAL mode.

b. FLOAT and 0 1 2... refer to other ways in which numbers are displayed. FLOAT mode is useful in hiding long decimal answers and will make some numbers clearer. It is best to leave this setting on FLOAT, except in applications such as money, where only two decimal places make more sense. Remember to change this setting back to FLOAT when you are done.

c. In this course you will use only the DEGREE mode. This setting is not important until you reach Chapter 11.

d. FUNCtion and PARametric are two different types of graphing modes. Most of the work in this course will be in FUNC mode.

e. SEQUENTIAL and SIMULtaneous tell the calculator to graph the equations one at a time, or to graph all the equations simultaneously.

f. Usually you'll want your screen set to FULL. Occasionally, after you have been working with a program, you may find that you are left with a split screen. If this happens, be sure to change this setting back to FULL.

The remaining settings in the mode screen are not important in this course. If you find that your screen looks very strange when you try to do something, it's a good idea to look at the mode screen and check to see if any settings have been changed.

Note 1B • Entering Lists

There are six pre-set lists in the calculator: lists L₁ through L₆. You can create other named lists if needed. You can enter 999 elements into a list if enough memory is available.

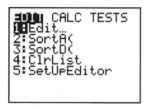

Clearing Data

If a list already has data in it, move the cursor up so that the list name is highlighted and press CLEAR ENTER.

Entering Data Directly into a List

Follow the steps below to enter data (such as 400, 455, 390, 450, 360, 320, 480, 480) into a list.

a. Press STAT 1 (Edit...).

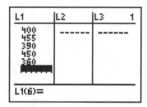

b. Enter each number into list L₁. If you do not see list L₁, see the sections **Resetting a List** or **Recalling a List** that follow. After entering each data value, press ENTER. When you are finished entering the data, press 2nd [QUIT]. If you wish to add a data value in the middle of the list, move the cursor to the place of insertion, press 2nd [INS], and then enter the number. To remove an entry from a list, highlight the entry and press DEL.

Entering Data into a List from the Home Screen

If you are working with a short list, you may want to enter it from the Home screen. To enter the data 1, 2, 3, 4 into list L₁ from the Home screen press 2nd [{] 1 [,] 2 [,] 3 [,] 4 2nd [}] STO▶ 2nd [L₁] ENTER.

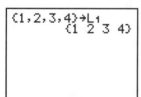 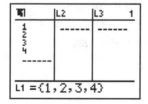

(continued)

You can also enter a list into the Home screen without storing it in a stat list.

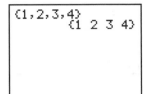

Naming a List

If you name a list, then you can save it for later use. To name a list, highlight the name of any list, for example L1, L2, and so on, and press 2nd [INS]. A new list will appear to the left of the list you highlighted. Enter a name for the list, for example, YEAR. (The flashing A tells you that you are in Alpha mode, so unless you want to enter a number as part of the name, you can just enter the list name.) Press ENTER and you will see that the list now has a name.

Resetting a List

To reset the calculator so that only lists L1 through L6 are displayed, press STAT and select 5:SetUpEditor. This action will not delete a named list from the calculator's memory and you will still be able to recall a named list with its stored data.

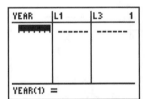   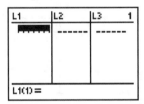

Deleting and Archiving a List on the TI-83 Plus or TI-84 Plus

To delete a list, press 2nd [MEM], select 2:Mem Mgnt/Del…, and then 4:List…, arrow to the list you want to delete, and press DEL. You can delete a pre-set list or a named list. If you delete a list, you lose the data in the list. To avoid losing the data, instead of pressing DEL, you can press ENTER to mark the list with an asterisk. This is called archiving and will temporarily disable the list(s) you mark. An archived list will not appear on the screen when you press STAT 1 (Edit…). By pressing 2nd [LIST] you can see that each archived list is preceded by an asterisk. An archived list retains its data but cannot be used until it is enabled. To enable an archived list, press 2nd [MEM] 2 (Mem Mgnt/Del…) 4 (List…), arrow to the list you want to enable, and press ENTER. The asterisk disappears. Press 2nd [QUIT] to return to the Home screen.

(continued)

```
MEMORY                RAM FREE    20261    RAM FREE    20373    NAMES OPS MATH
1:About               ARC FREE   147401    ARC FREE   147421    1:L1
2:Mem Mgmt/Del...     1:All...              L2        12       2:L2
3:Clear Entries       2:Real...             L3        12       3:L3
4:ClrAllLists         3:Complex...          L4        21       4:L4
5:Archive             4:List...            *L5        12       5:*L5
6:UnArchive           5:Matrix...           L6        12       6:L6
7↓Reset...            6↓Y-Vars...         ▶*YEAR      15       7:*YEAR
```

Deleting a List on the TI-83

To delete a list, press [2nd] [MEM], select 2:Delete..., and then 4:List..., arrow to the list you want to delete, and press [ENTER]. You can delete a pre-set list or a named list. If you delete a list, you lose the data in the list. Press [2nd] [QUIT] to return to the Home screen.

```
MEMORY                DELETE FROM...        DELETE:List          DELETE:List
1:Check RAM...        1:All...             L1         9         L1         9
2:Delete...           2:Real...            L2         9         L2         9
3:Clear Entries       3:Complex...         L3         9         L3         9
4:ClrAllLists         4:List...            L4        54         L4        54
5:Reset...            5:Matrix...          L5        63         L5        63
                      6:Y-Vars...         ▶L6        72        ▶DAY       11
                      7↓Prgm...            YEAR      12         MONTH     13
```

Recalling a List

Press [STAT] [1] (Edit...) to display the current lists. Next, create a blank, nameless list by highlighting a list name and pressing [2nd] [INS]. You now have a blank, nameless list ready to be named. To recall one of the pre-set lists (lists L_1 through L_6) that you previously deleted, press [2nd] [L1] or [2nd] [L2] and so on, and [ENTER]. The name is back, but not the data. (You can recall all deleted pre-set list names by using the **Resetting a List** procedure.) To recall a previously named list that was hidden from view by **Resetting a List,** press [2nd] [LIST], arrow down to the list you want to recall, and press [ENTER] [ENTER]. The list name and data reappear.

```
 L1    L2    L3    1    ____  L1    L2    1    NAMES OPS MATH     TDIST  L1    L2    1
____  ____  ____        ____  ____  ____       2↑L2               0     ____  ____
                                               3:L3               .2
                                               4:L4               .4
                                               5:L5               .6
                                               6:L6               .8
                                               7:DIST             1
L1 =                    Name=                   8:TDIST            1.2
                                                                  TDIST ={0,.2,.4,...
```

On the TI-83 Plus or TI-84 Plus, to recall a list that is archived, you must enable the list first and then recall it. Using the **Resetting a List** procedure will enable lists L_1 through L_6 whether they are archived or not.

Moving a List

To move a list, begin by highlighting the name of an empty list. Press [2nd] [LIST], arrow down to the name of the list you want to move, and press [ENTER] [ENTER]. The list data appears. You can now delete or overwrite the data in the original list, and the data will remain in the new list.

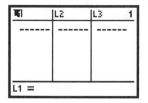
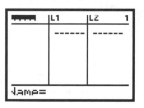

```
TDIST  DIST   L1    3    NAMES OPS MATH     TDIST  DIST   L1    3
0     .81688  ____        2↑L2              0     .81688  0
.2    .80995              3:L3              .2    .80995  .2
.4    .80918              4:L4              .4    .80918  .4
.6    .80861              5:L5              .6    .80861  .6
.8    .8119               6:L6              .8    .8119   .8
1     .80798              7:DIST            1     .80798  1
1.2   .80818              8:TDIST           1.2   .80818  1.2
L1 =                                        L1(1)=0
```

Note 1C • Median and Mean

Enter the data into a list, and return to the Home screen by pressing 2nd [QUIT].
(See **Note 1B** if you don't remember how to enter data into a list. The screen
here uses the same data as the first list entered in **Note 1B.**)

    a. Press 2nd [LIST] and arrow over to MATH.

    b. Choose 4:Median(or 3:Mean(.

```
NAMES OPS MATH
1:min(
2:max(
3■mean(
4:median(
5:sum(
6:prod(
7↓stdDev(
```

    c. Press 2nd [L1] (or whichever list contains the data) and close
       the parentheses.

    d. Press ENTER to find the value.

```
median(L1)
              425
mean(L1)
          416.875
```

You can also calculate all the statistical values of a data set at once, including
the median, mean, and the five summary values.

    a. Press STAT and arrow over to CALC.

    b. Choose 1:1–Var Stats.

```
EDIT CALC TESTS
1■1-Var Stats
2:2-Var Stats
3:Med-Med
4:LinReg(ax+b)
5:QuadReg
6:CubicReg
7↓QuartReg
```

    c. Press 2nd [L1] (or whichever list contains the data).

```
1-Var Stats L1
```

    d. Press ENTER.

(continued)

Use the down arrow to display the entire list of values.

$\bar{x} = 416.875$	the mean
$\Sigma x = 3335$	the sum of the x-values
$\Sigma x^2 = 1414425$	the sum of the squares of the x-values
$Sx = 58.73290025$	the sample standard deviation
$\sigma x = 54.93959751$	the population standard deviation
$n = 8$	the number of data values
$\text{minX} = 320$	the minimum data value
$Q1 = 375$	the first quartile
$\text{Med} = 425$	the median
$Q3 = 467.5$	the third quartile
$\text{maxX} = 480$	the maximum data value

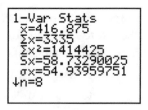

Errors

If you select 1–Var Stats and forget to enter the list name, the calculator default will be list L1. If you get ERR:INVALID DIM, you have selected a blank list.

Note 1D • Box Plots

Entering the Data

Enter the data set into a list. List L1 is used for this example. (See **Note 1B** if you need help entering data.)

Setting the WINDOW Values

Press WINDOW and enter the following values into the WINDOW screen.

Xmin = a number slightly less than the minimum of the data.

Xmax = a number slightly greater than the maximum of the data.

Xscl = the distance between tick marks. Although this number is not critical to graphing a box plot, if it's too small, the tick marks will make the x-axis appear too thick.

Ymin = 0.

Ymax = 10. This number is not important for a box plot. Any number greater than Ymin will work.

Yscl = 0. This number does not affect a box plot.

Xres = 1. This number does not affect a box plot.

(continued)

Displaying the Box Plot

This example uses the data in list L1, but you can choose any list.

   a. Clear or turn off any equations in the Y= screen. (Press [Y=]. Place the
   cursor anywhere in an equation and press [CLEAR] to delete the equation.
   Or, move the cursor over the highlighted equal sign of any equation
   you don't want to delete, and press [ENTER] to turn off the equation.)

   b. Press [2nd] [STAT PLOT] [1] (Plot1...). (You can choose any of the three
   stat plots.)

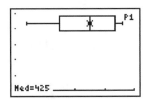

   c. Select On, Box Plot, L1, 1. (To select list L1 press [2nd] [L1].)

   Note that there are two types of box plots available. The first type will
   not connect outliers to the rest of the plot. The second type will. If you
   choose the first type, you will also have to indicate the mark you want
   to use for any outlying points.

   d. Press [GRAPH].

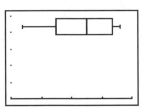

Tracing on a Box Plot

Press [TRACE]. The trace option allows you to see the five number summary
values for the box plot by pressing the left and right arrows. If you press the up
and down arrows, you move from one box plot to another. (See the **Graphing
More Than One Box Plot** section that follows.) Look in the upper-left corner
of the calculator screen to see which plot the calculator is tracing. The trace
option always starts with the stat plots and then moves to equations on the
Y= screen (if any are turned on), even if you can't see them in the current
window. Be sure to turn off any plots and any equations you do not want to
see or trace.

Graphing More Than One Box Plot

The calculator can graph up to three box plots at the same time. Follow the
directions for making a box plot and set up Plot2, Plot3, or both. Be sure the list
in which you've entered the data matches the list you select when setting up
each box plot.

Errors

If you don't see a graph, then check the Xmin and Xmax values to make sure
that your data lies between them. If you get ERR:INVALID DIM when you try to

(continued)

graph, you have selected a blank list. If you get ERR:WINDOW RANGE, you have probably assigned an Xmax value that is less than the Xmin value or a Ymax value that is less than the Ymin value.

Clean-up

When you are finished graphing box plots, you might want to turn off all the plots so that they don't interfere with other graphing screens. Press 2nd [STAT PLOT] 4 (PlotsOff) ENTER, or press Y=, arrow to any plot that is highlighted, and press ENTER.

Note 1E • Histograms

Entering the Data

Enter the data into a list. List L₁ is used for this example. (See **Note 1B** if you need help entering the data.)

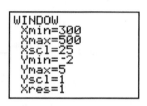

Setting the WINDOW Values

Press WINDOW and enter the following values into the WINDOW screen.

Xmin = a number equal to or slightly less than the minimum of the data.

Xmax = a number greater than the maximum of the data.

Xscl = the width of each bar. Use an integer value that is approximately equal to $\frac{Xmax - Xmin}{8}$.

Ymin = -2. Using a negative value for Ymin allows you to trace on the graph without the trace values interfering with the graph itself.

Ymax = the height of the tallest bar. Make an intelligent guess. You may have to revise this value when you look at the graph. Tracing on the graph can help you determine the maximum bar height.

Yscl = the distance between tick marks on the y-axis. The number you choose will depend on the Ymax value. You don't want tick marks that are too close together, or the y-axis will appear too thick.

Xres = 1. This number does not affect a histogram.

The Xscl value determines the width of the histogram bars. You may need to extend the range one bar-width beyond what you think it should be by increasing the Xmax value. You may want to create a histogram with as few as five or as many as ten bars. Experiment with different values for Xscl to see what effect each has on the graph.

(continued)

Displaying the Histogram

This example assumes the data is in list L1, but you can choose any list.

a. Clear or turn off any equations in the Y= screen. (Press [Y=]. Place the cursor anywhere in an equation and press [CLEAR] to delete the equation. Or, move the cursor over the highlighted equal sign of any equation you don't want to delete, and press [ENTER] to turn off the equation.)

b. Press [2nd] [STAT PLOT] [1] (Plot1...). (You can choose any of the three stat plots.)

c. Select On, Histogram, L1, 1. (To select list L1 press [2nd] [L1].)

d. Press [GRAPH].

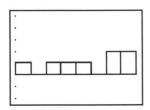

Tracing on a Histogram

Press [TRACE]. The trace option always starts with the stat plots and then moves to equations in the Y= screen (if any are turned on), even if you can't see them in the current window. Be sure to turn off any plots and any equations you do not want to see or trace.

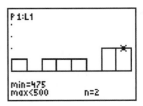

Errors

You will get ERR:STAT if you try to create a histogram with more than 47 intervals (bars). Make the Xscl value larger to correct this error. You may also get an error message if you haven't turned off a plot you're not interested in seeing or you have changed the data or the window settings.

Clean-up

When you are finished graphing histograms, you might want to turn off all the plots so that they don't interfere with other graphing screens. Press [2nd] [STAT PLOT] [4] (PlotsOff) [ENTER], or press [Y=], arrow to any plot that is highlighted, and press [ENTER].

Note 1F • Scatter Plots

Entering the Data

Enter the x-coordinates (horizontal axis) into one list and the y-coordinates (vertical axis) into another list. List L1 and list L2 are used for this example. (See **Note 1B** if you need help entering the data.)

(continued)

Setting the WINDOW Values

Press WINDOW and enter the following values into the WINDOW screen.

Xmin = a number less than the minimum value in the list of *x*-coordinates.

Xmax = a number greater than the maximum value in the list of *x*-coordinates.

Xscl = the distance between tick marks. You can use 0 (no tick marks) or a value usually less than or equal to $\frac{Xmax - Xmin}{10}$. If your Xscl value is too small, the *x*-axis will appear too thick.

Ymin = a number less than the minimum value in the list of *y*-coordinates.

Ymax = a number greater than the maximum value in the list of *y*-coordinates.

Yscl = the distance between tick marks. You can use 0 (no tick marks) or a value usually less than or equal to $\frac{Ymax - Ymin}{10}$. If your Yscl value is too small, the *y*-axis will appear too thick.

Xres = 1. This number does not affect a scatter plot.

Displaying the Scatter Plot

a. Clear or turn off any equations in the Y= screen. (Press Y=. Place the cursor anywhere in an equation and press CLEAR to delete the equation. Or, move the cursor over the highlighted equal sign of any equation you don't want to delete, and press ENTER to turn off the equation.)

b. Press 2nd [STAT PLOT] 1 (Plot1...). (You can choose any of the three stat plots.)

c. Select On, ScatterPlot, L1 for Xlist (if your *x*-coordinates are in list L1); L2 for Ylist (if your *y*-coordinates are in list L2), and choose a mark type to indicate the data points.

d. Press GRAPH.

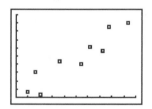

Tracing on a Scatter Plot

Press TRACE. The trace option always starts with the stat plots and then moves to equations in the Y= screen (if any are turned on), even if you can't see them in the current window. Be sure to turn off any plots and any equations you do not want to see or trace.

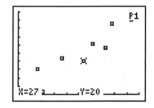

(continued)

Graphing More Than One Scatter Plot at a Time

The calculator can graph up to three scatter plots at the same time. Follow the directions for displaying a scatter plot and set up Plot2, Plot3, or both. Be sure the lists in which you've entered the data match the lists you select when setting up each scatter plot. Be sure to choose a different mark for each plot.

Errors

An ERR:DIM MISMATCH message means that the two lists do not have the same number of entries. This could also happen if you left a stat plot on that you're not using, or if you named the wrong list when you set up the scatter plot.

If the graph does not look like you think it should, try any (or all) of the following: Clear or turn off all equations in the Y= screen. Press 2nd [FORMAT] and select GridOff. Press MODE and check that the calculator is set to Func.

Clean-up

When you are finished graphing scatter plots, you might want to turn off all the plots so that they don't interfere with other graphing screens. Press 2nd [STAT PLOT] 4 (PlotsOff) ENTER or press Y=, arrow to any plot that is highlighted, and press ENTER.

Note 1G • POINTS Program

First, link or manually enter the program into your calculator. (See **Note 0F** or **Note 0G.**) The POINTS program plots a single point in a graphing window that measures from –4.7 to 4.7 on the horizontal axis and from –3.1 to 3.1 on the vertical axis. You identify and enter the coordinates of the point rounded to the nearest 0.5 units.

    a. To execute the program, press PRGM, arrow to POINTS, press ENTER twice, and then press 1 or ENTER to select 1:PLAY.

    b. Study the screen and determine the coordinates of the marked point.

    c. Press ENTER.

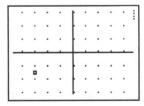

    d. Enter the x-coordinate, a comma, the y-coordinate, and close the parentheses. Then press ENTER.

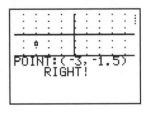

(continued)

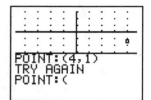

e. If you enter the wrong coordinates, repeat **step d** and enter new values.

f. If you enter the wrong coordinates a second time, the calculator will display the correct answer.

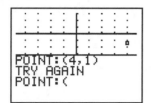 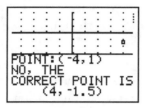

g. Press ENTER to display another point.

h. When you are ready to quit the program, enter 0 and press ENTER.

Errors

If you get ERR:SYNTAX, select 1:Quit and start the program over by pressing ENTER. To change your screen back to a full screen, press MODE and highlight Full.

Clean-up

If you quit POINTS without using the QUIT option in the program, you might be left with a split screen. Press MODE and select Full. Press 2nd [FORMAT] and select GridOff. Press 2nd [STAT PLOT] 4 (PlotsOff) ENTER, or press Y=, arrow to any plot that is turned on, and press ENTER.

```
PROGRAM:POINTS
3→W:Lbl 1
Full:PlotsOff
FnOff :GridOn
randInt(-9,9,1)/2→L₁
randInt(-6,6,1)/2→L₂
Plot1(Scatter,L₁,L₂,□)
ZDecimal:Pause
Lbl 2:Horiz
Output(4,1,"USE 0 TO QUIT")
Repeat W≠1
Input "POINT:(",Str1
inString(Str1,",")→C
If C=0:Goto 9
inString(Str1,")")→P
If P=0:length(Str1)+1→P
sub(Str1,1,C-1)→Str2
sub(Str1,C+1,P-C-1)→Str3
String▶Equ(Str2,Y₂)
String▶Equ(Str3,Y₃)
FnOff
L₁(1)→X:L₂(1)→Y
```

```
If Y₂=X and Y₃=Y:Then
Disp "    RIGHT!"
0→W:Pause
Else:If W=1
Then
Disp "NO, THE"
Disp "CORRECT POINT IS"
Output(4,1,"    (")
Output(4,6,X)
7+(X<0)+2(fPart(X)≠0)→H
Output(4,H,",")
Output(4,H+1,Y)
H+2+(Y<0)+2(fPart(Y)≠0)→K
Output(4,K,")")
2→W:Pause
Else:1→W
Disp "TRY AGAIN"
End:End:End
Goto 1
Lbl 9:Full:GridOff:PlotsOff
Disp "PRESS ENTER","TO REPLAY.","",
    "PRESS 1","AND ENTER","TO QUIT."
```

Note 1H • Connecting the Points

The xyLine connects a sequence of points with line segments. The order in which the points are connected is the order in which the coordinates appear in the lists.

Enter data and set the window as described in **Note 1F.**

Displaying the Connected Points

a. Clear or turn off any equations in the Y= screen. (Press Y=. Place the cursor anywhere in an equation and press CLEAR to delete the equation. Or, move the cursor over the highlighted equal sign of any equation that you don't want to delete, and press ENTER to turn off the equation.)

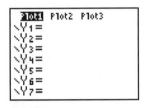

b. Press 2nd [STAT PLOT] 1 (Plot1...). (You can choose any of the three stat plots.)

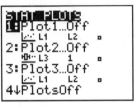

c. Select On, xyLine, L1 for Xlist (if your *x*-coordinates are in list L1), L2 for Ylist (if your *y*-coordinates are in list L2), and choose a mark type to indicate the data points.

d. Press GRAPH.

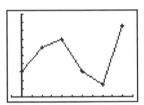

If the points are not listed in ascending order by their *x*-coordinates, your xyLine will be scrambled with the line segments criss-crossing each other. To reorder your points correctly, go to the Home screen and press STAT and select 2:Sort A(. Complete the command Sort (L1, L2) and press ENTER. Notice that the sort command puts list L1 in ascending order but maintains the original pairings between list L1 and list L2. (See **Note 10B.**)

Tracing Connected Points

Press TRACE. The trace option always starts with the stat plots and then moves to equations in the Y= screen (if any are turned on), even if you can't see them in the current window. Be sure to turn off any plots and any equations you do not want to see or trace.

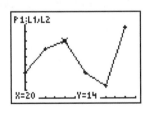

(continued)

 ****

Errors

An ERR:DIM MISMATCH message means that the two lists do not have the same number of entries. This could also happen if you left a plot on that you're not using, or if you named the wrong list when you set up the xyLine.

If the graph does not look like you think it should, try one (or all) of the following: Clear or turn off all equations on the Y= screen. Press 2nd [FORMAT] and select GridOff. Press MODE and make sure the calculator is set to Func and to Full.

Clean-up

When you are finished with the xyLine, you might want to turn off all the plots so that they don't interfere with other graphing screens. Press 2nd [STAT PLOT] 4 (PlotsOff) ENTER or press Y=, arrow to any plot that is highlighted, and press ENTER.

Note 1I/App • Reading a Distance Using the EasyData App

You must have a TI-83 Plus or TI-84 Plus to use this Note. If you have a TI-83 and a CBR, see **Note 1I** below.

You will need a CBR (Calculator-Based Ranger).

Connect the CBR to the calculator. Press APPS and select EasyData. The CBR will immediately begin collecting distance data, which is displayed on your calculator screen. Press Quit (GRAPH) then OK (GRAPH again) to stop collecting data.

Note 1I • Reading a Distance Using the DIST Program

Follow the instructions in this note if you have a CBR (Calculator-Based Ranger) and a TI-83. If you are using a TI-83 Plus or TI-84 Plus with CBR or CBL, use the EasyData App described in **Note 1I/App** above.

You will need the DIST program. To link this program from another calculator, see **Note 0F.** If you must manually enter the program, see **Note 0G.**

   a. Connect your CBR to a graphing calculator using the calculator-to-CBR cable. Push in the cable firmly at both ends.

   b. Execute the program by pressing PRGM, then arrow down to DIST, and press ENTER twice.

   c. While the program is running, the calculator will continue to read distances from the CBR.

   d. Press ON and select 1:Quit to stop the program.

(continued)

```
PROGRAM:DIST
Full
ClrHome
Disp "NOW CHECKING THE"
Disp "CALCULATOR-CBR"
Disp "LINK CONNECTION."
Disp "PLEASE WAIT...."
{1,0}→L₁
Send {L₁}
{0}→L₂
Lbl M
{7}→L₁
Send(L₁)
Get(L₂)
If  dim(L₂)=1 and  L₂(1)=0
Then
ClrHome
Disp "***LINK  ERROR***"
Disp "PUSH  IN  THE  LINK"
Disp "CORD CONNECTORS"
Disp "FIRMLY  THEN  HIT"
Disp "[ENTER]."
Pause

Goto M
End
Disp " "
Output(6,1," STATUS: O.K.")
Output(8,10,"[ENTER]")
Pause
Full
ClrHome

Disp "PRESS [ENTER] TO"
Disp "BEGIN"
Disp " "
Disp " "
Disp "PRESS [ON] TO"
Disp "QUIT"
Pause
Lbl 1
{3,2,2,0}→L₁
Send(L₁)
Get(L₁)
Disp round (L₁(2),2)
Goto 1
```

Errors

If you are not getting a reading, make sure the link cable is connected tightly at both ends. If the cable is secure, try changing the batteries in the CBR.

Note 1J • Equations

To graph an equation on your calculator, the equation must be in the form $y =$ "some expression." If the equation contains variables other than x and y, you need to rewrite it using only x and y as variables.

    a. Press Y=.

    b. Enter the equation using the variable x. Press X,T,θ,n to enter the variable x.

    c. Setting a window for graphing equations is not as easy as setting a window for data. If it is an application problem, think about what values make sense for both x and y. You may need to try different windows to find one that is appropriate.

    d. Press GRAPH.

Tracing Equations and Plots on the Same Graph

Enter the data and set up a scatter plot. Enter the equation. Set the window. You can do these three steps in any order. When you press GRAPH, you will see the stat plot graphed first and the equation(s) graphed second. When you press TRACE, you will first trace the data in the stat plot. Press the down arrow to trace

(continued)

other stat plots if they are turned on. By arrowing down again you will trace any equations that are turned on. Note the label in the upper left corner of the screen. The label P1 indicates that you are tracing Plot1. The labels L1 and L2 indicate that the data comes from list L1 and list L2. When you are tracing on an equation, the equation is displayed.

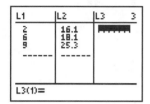
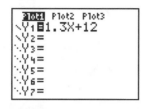
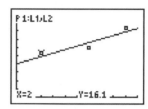

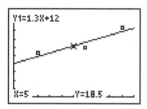

If you don't see P1:L1,L2 or the equation, press 2nd [FORMAT] and select ExprOn. If ExprOn is not turned on, you will see a P1, P2, 1, 2, and so on, in the upper-right corner of the screen, but you will not see which lists are being plotted or the actual equation.

Errors

If you get an ERR: DIM MISMATCH message, turn off all the stat plots. Press 2nd [STAT PLOT] 4 (PlotsOff) ENTER or press Y=, arrow to any plot that is highlighted, and press ENTER. If you see ERR: SYNTAX, check your equation and count the number of left and right parentheses to make sure they match. Look for numbers with two decimal points. Check that you used the negative or subtraction sign correctly. If you see the graph screen but nothing appears, you might have a problem with your equation or your window. Try changing one or both of these.

Note 1K • Formula-Generated Lists

Enter data into a list as in **Note 1B.** Move the cursor to the next list, arrow up to highlight the list name, and press ENTER. Enter the formula for the operations you wish to perform, such as 2nd [L1] + 4 7. Then press ENTER. If you get an error message, select 2:Goto and press CLEAR. Make sure you are on the name of the list before you enter the list operation. You can do operations with list variables the same way you do with numbers. You can add, subtract, multiply, divide, or do any other mathematical operation.

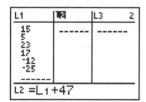

(continued)

For another example, let list L_1 be a list of rectangle lengths and let list L_2 be the corresponding widths. Move the cursor so that it highlights list L_3 and enter the formula for the area of a rectangle, $L_1 * L_2$. Press ENTER.

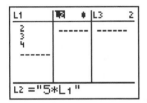 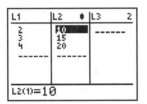

List Formulas

If you enclose a formula in quotation marks (press ALPHA ["]), the entries of the new list will automatically update if you change the values in the list referred to in the formula. For example, let list L_1 be 2, 3, 4, and define the name of list L_2 to be $5 * L_1$. Notice the mark to the right of list L_2 that indicates a formula name. Now edit one of the entries in list L_1, for example, change the 3 to 5. Notice that the second entry in list L_2 automatically updates to 25.

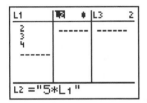 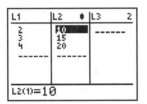 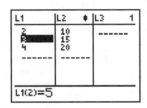 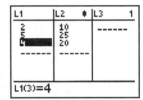

To delete a formula move up to the list name and press ENTER. Then press CLEAR once to remove the formula but keep the list values. Press ENTER. Repeat this process a second time to remove the list values.

Errors

You will get an error if you clear a list that is used in defining a formula-generated list. Select 2:Goto and press CLEAR.

Note 1L • Matrices

The matrix menu allows you to work with up to ten matrices, $[A], [B], \ldots, [J]$. The dimensions of a matrix are the number of rows by the number of columns, that is, $r \times c$. The dimensions are limited to 99 rows and 99 columns or, more likely, by the memory available in your calculator.

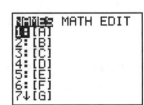

Entering a Matrix

The matrix EDIT menu allows you to construct and store a matrix. Press 2nd [MATRIX] and arrow to EDIT. (On the TI-83, press MATRX and arrow to EDIT.) Press 1 to edit the dimensions of [A] and to enter the matrix values. Notice that as you press ENTER for each dimension, the matrix on the screen adjusts its size. Continue to enter each value into the matrix. Press ENTER after each entry and the cursor moves across the row and then down to the next row. The current position of the cursor and the cell value is shown by $r, c = value$ in the bottom-left corner of the screen. You can edit any entry by arrowing to the position and reentering the value. After you have entered all of the values, press 2nd [QUIT] to store the matrix.

(continued)

Enter [A] to have dimensions 6 × 2.

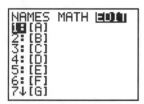 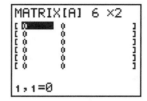 

Displaying a Matrix

Press 2nd [MATRIX] to see which matrices are stored in the calculator. (On the TI-83, press MATRX to see which matrices are stored in the calculator.) You can see the dimensions of each stored matrix. To display the name [A] on the Home screen, press 2nd [MATRIX] 1. (On the TI-83, to display the name [A] on the Home screen, press MATRX 1.) Press ENTER to display the actual matrix.

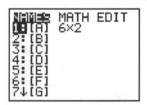 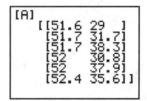

If you want a matrix to represent money, you can set the calculator so that all numbers show two decimal places. Press MODE and change the setting on the second line from Float to 2. All calculator numbers will now display two decimal places.

Deleting a Matrix from the Calculator

You can always change a matrix by arrowing to EDIT in the matrix menu and selecting the matrix you want to change. You might, however, want to conserve memory space and delete a matrix completely from your calculator. To delete a matrix, press 2nd [MEM] 2 (Delete...) 5 (Matrix...), arrow to the matrix you want to delete, and press ENTER.

(continued)

Errors

If you get an ERR:MEMORY message, you've tried to enter matrix dimensions
that exceed the available memory in the calculator.

An ERR:UNDEFINED message probably indicates that you have named a matrix
that is not defined.

Note 1M • Multiplying a Matrix by a Number

To multiply a matrix by a number, multiply each cell value of the matrix by the
number. For example, if [A] is the matrix from **Note 1L,** to multiply [A] by 50,
enter 50 ∗ [A] or 50[A] on the Home screen and press ENTER. The matrix answer
appears on the screen.

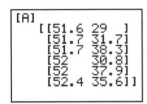  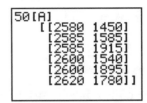

Multiplying a number by a matrix, [A] ∗ 50 for example, is done in the same way.

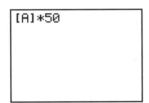 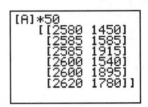

Errors

An ERR:UNDEFINED message probably indicates that you have named a matrix
that is not defined.

Note 1N • Adding/Subtracting Matrices

To add or subtract two matrices, the matrices must have the same dimensions.
Define [B] to have dimensions 3 × 2, and enter the values below. (See **Note 1L.**)

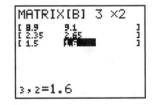

$1, 1 = 8.9$　　　$1, 2 = 9.1$

$2, 1 = 2.35$　　$2, 2 = 2.65$

$3, 1 = 1.5$　　　$3, 2 = 1.6$

Define [C] to have dimensions 3 × 2, and enter the values below.

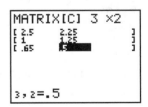

$1, 1 = 2.5$　　$1, 2 = 2.25$

$2, 1 = 1$　　　$2, 2 = 1.25$

$3, 1 = .65$　　$3, 2 = .5$

(continued)

On a clear Home screen, enter [B] + [C] and press ENTER. The matrix showing on the screen is the sum of [B] and [C].

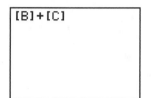

Errors

If you get ERR:DIM MISMATCH, you've tried to add (or subtract) two matrices that don't have the same dimensions.

An ERR:UNDEFINED message probably indicates that you have named a matrix that is not defined.

Note 1P • Multiplying Two Matrices

To multiply two matrices, the number of columns in the first matrix must match the number of rows in the second matrix. For example, if the first matrix has dimensions 1 × 3 and the second matrix has dimensions 3 × 2, the three columns of the first matrix match the three rows of the second. The multiplication will be defined.

Enter [D] and [C] as shown in the screens here. (See **Note 1L.**)

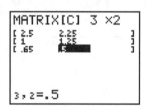

Display [D] [C] (or [D] * [C]) on the Home screen and press ENTER. The product appears on the screen. The dimensions of the product are (*the number of rows of the first matrix*) × (*the number of columns of the second matrix*). In this example, a 1 × 3 matrix times a 3 × 2 matrix has a 1 × 2 answer.

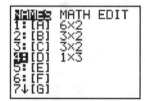
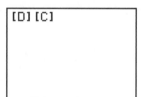
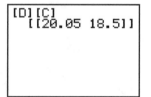

Errors

If you get ERR:DIM MISMATCH, then the number of columns in the first matrix does not match the number of rows in the second.

An ERR:UNDEFINED message probably indicates that you have named a matrix that is not defined.

Note 2A • Tables

Once you have entered an equation into the Y= screen, you can create a table of values based on that equation.

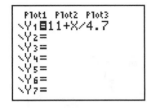

Step 1: Enter the equation(s) into the Y= screen. (See **Note 1J.**)

Step 2: Press 2nd [TBLSET].

   a. TblStart is the first *x*-coordinate you want to see in the table.

   b. ΔTbl is the amount of increase or decrease between the *x*-coordinates in the table.

   c. Select Auto for both Indpnt and Depend. (Use Ask for Indpnt to build a table where you enter *x*-coordinates one at a time.) Usually you will leave both of these settings on Auto.

Step 3: Press 2nd [TABLE].

   a. You can scroll up and down the *x*-coordinates to search for a particular *y*-coordinate.

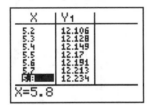

   b. You can arrow over to the *y*-column to see the number more accurately displayed (if necessary) at the bottom of the screen.

   c. You can arrow up and highlight the Y₁ header to see the equation displayed at the bottom of the screen.

   d. If you press ENTER while you are looking at the function, you can edit the equation and see the changes in the table. This action will also change the equation in the Y= screen.

(continued)

Table Zooming

When you are searching for a particular y-coordinate that does not appear to be in the table, you can use a technique called "table zooming." Let's suppose you enter the equation $Y_1 = 11 + X/4.7$ and you want to find the x-coordinate that corresponds to a y-coordinate of 20, but 20 is not in the current table.

a. Press [2nd] [TBLSET].

b. Start with a guess for a reasonably close x-coordinate and enter that value in TblStart, in this case, 0, and then enter a large value in ΔTbl, such as 10.

c. Look for y-coordinates on either side of your search value. Arrow so that the value just less than your search value is at the top of the list.

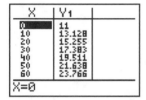 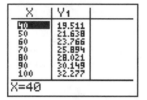 

d. Return to [2nd] [TBLSET] and reduce ΔTbl by a factor of 10. Notice that the value you put at the top of the list is now in TblStart.

e. Go back to step c and repeat until you have found the search value, in this case, 20.

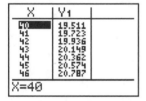 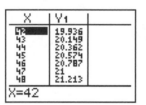  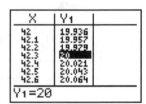

Note 2B • INVERSE Program

You will need a CBR (Calculator-Based Ranger). Connect the CBR to the calculator.

This program will record total time and average speed for six walks. For each walk, the motion sensor (CBR) is set to wait for its trigger to be pressed, then it records a walker's speed for ten seconds. When the trigger is pressed, the walker should wait for a second or two, then walk two meters at a constant speed. The walker should come to a complete stop after walking the two meters and not move for the remainder of the ten seconds.

 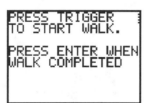

(continued)

Once the speed data is graphed, you'll mark the beginning of the walk (when the speed begins to increase), and the end of the walk (when the speed returns to zero). To do this, use the right arrow to move to the beginning of the walk and press ENTER. Then right arrow to the end of the walk and press enter. The calculator will then show just the selected portion of the graph and ask, "Is this correct?" Select Y or N. If you select N, you'll get another try.

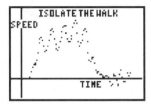 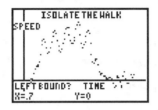 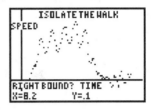 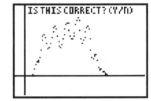

The calculator will show the elapsed time for the walk (maximum time − minimum time) and the average of the speed (velocity) over this interval. Record this information in a data table. The time is measured in seconds and the speed is measured in meters per second. The program will repeat these steps six times.

```
WALK NUMBER
            1.000
max(TIME)-min(T...
            6.896
mean(VELOCITY)
            .262
    --ENTER--
```

```
PROGRAM:INVERSE
Disp " TIME and SPEED"," ","WALKER
    AT START","LINE. CBR 1M","BEHIND
    THE LINE.","WALKER BEGINS","AFTER
    CBR STARTS"
{0}→L₁:{0}→L₂
Output(8,1,"  --ENTER--")
Pause
For(N,1,6)
Send({0})
Send({1,11,2,1,0,0})
Send({3,0.1,100,1,0,0,0,0,1,2})
ClrHome
Disp "PRESS TRIGGER","TO START
    WALK."," ","PRESS ENTER
    WHEN","WALK COMPLETED."
ExprOff
Pause
Send({5,11,1})
Get(L₄)
Get(L₃)
Repeat K=92
PlotsOff
Plot1(Scatter,L₃,L₄,·)
```

```
ZoomStat
Text(0,20,"ISOLATE THE WALK")
Text(8,0,"SPEED")
Text(50,50,"TIME")
Select(L₅,L₆)
Text(0,10,"IS THIS CORRECT? (Y/N)")
Repeat K=92 or K=71
getKey→K
End:End
ClrHome
max(L₅)-min(L₅)→L₁(N)
Disp "WALK NUMBER",N
Disp "max(TIME)-min(TIME)",L₁(N)
mean(L₆)→L₂(N)
Disp "mean(VELOCITY)",L₂(N)
Pause "  --ENTER--"
End
Plot1(Scatter,L₁,L₂,□)
ZoomStat
0→Xmin:0→Ymin
Text(8,3,"SPEED")
Text(50,50,"TIME")
1/L₂→L₃
```

Note 2C • Instant Replay

Whenever you enter a command or expression into your calculator, it is filed and can usually be retrieved. The simplest filing is the Home screen command buffer. When you enter a command or expression into the Home screen, you can recall it by pressing [2nd] [ENTRY]. Then, you can edit the command or expression by highlighting what you want to change and pressing [DEL] to delete and/or [2nd] [INS] to insert to the left.

```
3(4-5)+15
             12
3(■-5)+15
```

```
3(4-5)+15
             12
3(8-5)+15
             24
```

```
3(4-5)+15
             12
3(8-5)+15
             24
3(8-25)+15
            -36
```

Note 3A • Recursion on a List

Refer to **Note 0D** to review recursion and **Note 1B** to review entering a list into the Home screen.

```
{0,4}
                    {0 4}
Ans(2)
                      4
```

When defining a recursive routine, the value for the last answer can come either from a list or it can be a single number, as in **Note 0D.** If you want to generate two patterns at once or keep track of the term numbers of a sequence, using recursion on a list can be useful. When using recursion on a list, you must refer to the number of the term in the list that you want to use. So, Ans(2) does not mean the last answer times 2, but rather the value of the second term in the previous list.

To use recursion on a list, enter a list of initial values and press ENTER. The list must be enclosed in braces. Then create a formula line that is a list, with each term being a formula using the value of a term(s) in the original list. Finally, press ENTER repeatedly to generate a sequence of lists.

```
{1,4}
                    {1 4}
{Ans(1)+1,Ans(2)
+7}
                   {2 11}
                   {3 18}
                   {4 25}
```

The screen here shows a sequence of lists, each containing two terms. The pattern of the first term in each list is a sequence that starts with 1 and increases by 1 each time. This sequence gives an index number for the second term in each list. The pattern of the second terms in the lists is a sequence that starts with 4 and increases by 7 each time. So, for example, {4 25} indicates that 25 is the fourth term in the sequence that begins with 4 and increases by 7 with each new term.

Note 3B/App • Collecting Distance Data Using the EasyData App

You must have a TI-83 Plus or TI-84 Plus to use this Note. If you have a TI-83, see **Note 3B** on pages 32–33. You can also use the programs CBRSET and CBRGET with any calculator. See page vi.

You will need a CBR (Calculator-Based Ranger).

Connect the CBR to the calculator. Press APPS and select EasyData. The CBR will immediately begin collecting distance data, which is displayed on your calculator screen.

To collect distance data, press Setup (WINDOW) and select 2:Time Graph…. You will be shown the default settings for time interval and number of samples. Press Edit (ZOOM) to edit these settings. Enter 0.2 for the sample interval and press Next. Enter 30 for the number of samples and press Next. Then press OK.

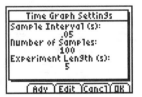

The calculator will resume collecting data. Press Start (ZOOM) to collect the 6 seconds of data you have specified. You will be told that this function will overwrite the current list data. Press OK to continue. The calculator will collect the data and graph it.

(continued)

To end the Application, press Main then press Quit. You will get a message telling you where the data is stored. Time data is in L1, distance data is in L6, velocity data is in L7, and acceleration data is in L8.

 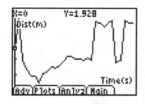 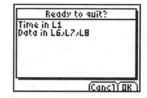

When you press STAT, then select 1:Edit, L1 and L6 are shown (you'll need to arrow to the right to see L6.) If you want to see L7 and L8, you'll need to recall those lists. See **Note 1B** for help recalling or moving a list.

Note 3B • WALKER Program

This program can be used with the TI-83, TI-83 Plus, and TI-84 Plus. However, if you have a TI-83 Plus or TI-84 Plus, you should consider using the EasyData App described in **Note 3B/App** on the preceding page.

This program will collect and graph distance-time data or velocity-time data using a motion sensor. Each WALK command allows you to see the graph being constructed as the data are collected. To start, you must select one of the following commands.

1:FREE FORM gives you a blank screen for simple data collection.

2:WALK LINE draws a random line for you to try to walk.

3:WALK PATH draws a random path of three segments for you to match.

4:WALK FUNCTION expects you to enter an equation into Y1 *before* you start the program and then to match the path it makes.

5:WALK SPEED graphs meters per second and time. You must try to match three horizontal segments.

6:REPEAT LAST repeats the previous command on the same graph.

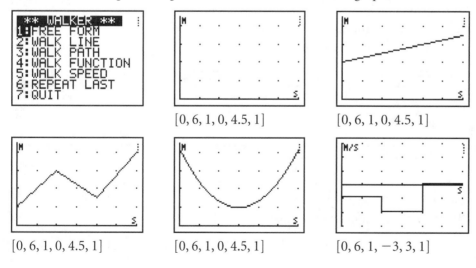

$[0, 6, 1, 0, 4.5, 1]$ $[0, 6, 1, 0, 4.5, 1]$

$[0, 6, 1, 0, 4.5, 1]$ $[0, 6, 1, 0, 4.5, 1]$ $[0, 6, 1, -3, 3, 1]$

(continued)

```
PROGRAM:WALKER
Full
ClrHome
Disp "NOW CHECKING THE"
Disp "CALCULATOR-CBR"
Disp "LINK CONNECTION."
Disp "PLEASE WAIT...."
{1,0}→L₁
Send(L₁)
{0}→L₂
Lbl M
{7}→L₁
Send(L₁)
Get(L₂)
If dim(L₂)=1 and L₂(1)=0
Then
ClrHome
Disp "***LINK ERROR***"
Disp "PUSH IN THE LINK"
Disp "CORD CONNECTORS"
Disp "FIRMLY THEN HIT"
Disp "[ENTER]."
Pause
Goto M
End
Disp ""
Output(6,1," STATUS: O.K.")
Output(8,10,"[ENTER]")
Pause
6→T:4→D:20→R
{47,20,6}→LWDFT
1/R→I
{1,0}→LCLEAR
{1,11,2}→LSONIC
{3,I,⁻1,0}→LREAD
GridOn:Func
FnOff
Lbl 0:0→F :
PlotsOff 1:FnOff
Menu(" ** WALKER ** ","FREE
   FORM",7,"WALK LINE",8,"WALK
   PATH",1,"WALK FUNCTION",F,"WALK
   SPEED",2,"REPEAT LAST",3,"QUIT",4)
Lbl F:FnOn 1:99→U
Lbl 7:2→F
Lbl 8:F-1→F
Lbl 1
0→Xmin:T→Xmax
0→Ymin:D+.5→Ymax
1→Xscl:1→Yscl
```

```
PlotsOff
randInt(1,20,4)/2→L₄
{0,T/3,2T/3,T}→L₃
If F=⁻1:3L₃→L₃
Plot2(xyLine,L₃,L₄,.)
If F=1:PlotsOff
Lbl 5
ClrDraw:DispGraph
Text(0,2,"M")
Text(55,83,"S")
Lbl 9:Pause
Send(LCLEAR)
Send(LSONIC)
Send(LREAD)
int(RT)+1→N
N→dim(L₂)
For(J,2,N)
Get(L₂(J))
L₂(J)→X:If  F=2:7(X-L₂(J-1))→X
Pt-On(I(J-1),X)
End:Send(LCLEAR)
seq(IJ,J,0,N-1)→L₁
Pause
Plot1(Scatter,L₁,L₂,.)
Goto 0
Lbl 2:2→F
GridOff
0→Xmin:⁻3→Ymin
T→Xmax:3→Ymax
1→Xscl:1→Yscl
PlotsOff
randInt(0,4,6)-1.9→L₄
L₄(1)→L₄(2)
L₄(3)→L₄(4)
L₄(5)→L₄(6)
{0,2,2,4,4,6}→L₃
Plot2(xyLine,L₃,L₄,.)
Lbl 6:2→F
ClrDraw
DispGraph:
Text(0,2,"M/S")
Text(32,83,"S")
Goto 9
Lbl 3
If U=99:Then:FnOn :1→U:End
If Ymin=0:Goto 5
Goto 6
Lbl 4
ClrHome
```

Note 3C • INOUT Program

In this program, you write a linear rule or expression that links a set of input values to their corresponding output values. Before executing the program, choose a level of difficulty that is easy, medium, or hard. We recommend that you choose "EASY" until you get a string of rules correct on the first try. If you make an incorrect guess, the program displays your results and allows you to try again. In the beginning, enter your guess in the form $a + b \cdot$ L₁, where a is the starting value and b is the recursive rule. Later you may wish to write your rule in other ways. But always use list L₁ as the variable in your expression. List L₁ is the input list.

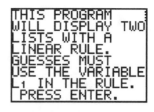

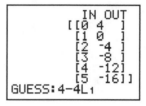

```
PROGRAM:INOUT
0→R
ClrHome
Disp "THIS PROGRAM.","WILL DISPLAY
    TWO","LISTS WITH A ", "LINEAR
    RULE. ","GUESSES MUST","USE THE
    VARIABLE","L₁ IN THE RULE."
Output(8,2,"PRESS ENTER."):Pause
Lbl 0
Menu("INOUT PROGRAM","EASY",1,
    "MEDIUM",2, "HARD",3,"QUIT",Q)
Lbl 1
{0,1,2,3,4,5}→L₁
randInt(⁻5,5,2)→L₄
Goto 5
Lbl 2
seq(X,X,⁻3,8)→L₁
rand (12)→L₂
SortA(L₂,L₁)
6→dim(L₁)
SortA(L₁)
randInt(⁻7,7,2)→L₄
Goto 5
Lbl 3
seq(X,X,⁻9,9,.5)→L₁
rand (37)→L₂
SortA(L₂,L₁)
6→dim(L₁)
```

```
randInt(⁻9,9,2)→L₄
Lbl 5
ClrHome
L₄(1)L₁+L₄(2)→L₂
List▸matr(L₁,L₂,[A])
Disp "    IN  OUT"
Disp [A]
Repeat sum(L₃-L₂)=0
If R:Then
Input "START VALUE:",S
Input "CHANGE:",C
S+CL₁→L₃
Else
Input "GUESS:",L₃
End
List▸matr(L₁,L₂,L₃,[A])
ClrHome
Disp " IN   OUT   YOU"
Disp [A]
End
Output(8,3,"RIGHT!")
Pause
Goto 0
Lbl Q:ClrHome
Disp "  PRESS ENTER","   TO
    REPLAY","","    PRESS","    1 AND
    ENTER","   TO QUIT"
```

To enter [A], press 2nd [MATRIX] and choose [A]; don't use 2nd [or ALPHA A.

Note 3D • LINES Program

You can use this program to practice writing the equation for a line. Before you begin, clear any equations in the Y= screen, and set the graph style to "line with trail" by moving to the left of Y₁ and pressing ENTER four times. When you run the program, the graph of a line will appear. In the "EASY" option, the

(continued)

y-intercept will always appear on the screen. In the "HARD" option, the
y-intercept may or may not appear on the screen.

Run the program and follow these steps:

a. Press 1 ENTER to select the "EASY" option, or 2 ENTER to select the
"HARD" option.

b. Press ENTER to see the graph.

c. Study the graph and determine values that will help you write the
equation for the line. You can trace on the line to see the coordinates of
individual points.

d. Press Y= and enter the linear equation that you think matches the line
on the graph.

e. Press GRAPH to compare the graph of your line to the program's line.

f. If the two lines don't match, repeat **steps c, d,** and **e** until they do. You
can enter new equations for other Y= lines or you can clear your old
guess before you enter a new one.

g. When the graphs match, you will see them as one line. Trace and
switch from one line to the other. The equation in the upper-left corner
will indicate whether there really are two lines. Pressing ENTER after
you've traced a line will only regraph that same line.

h. When you are finished, press 2nd [QUIT]. Press ENTER, then press 1 or
2 and ENTER to replay, or 3 ENTER to quit.

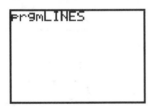 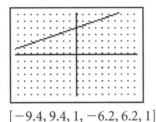 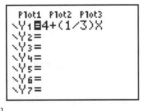 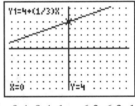

$[-9.4, 9.4, 1, -6.2, 6.2, 1]$ $[-9.4, 9.4, 1, -6.2, 6.2, 1]$

Clean-Up

When you are finished running the program, you will probably want to turn
the grid off. You should also turn the expressions off. Press 2nd [FORMAT] and
select GridOff and ExprOff. You might also want to clear an equation that is
hidden in the Y= screen in Y₀.

```
PROGRAM:LINES                      - 6 . 2 → Y m i n : 6 . 2 → Y m a x
ClrHome                            ClrHome
0 → A                              Disp "PRESS ENTER","TO CONTINUE."
Menu("LINES",                      If A=1:randInt(-9,8)→A
  "EASY",1,"HARD",2,"QUIT",3)      randInt(A+1,9)→C
Lbl 2:1→A                          randInt(-6,6)→B
Lbl 1                              randInt(-6,6)→D
Disp "PRESS ENTER.", "TO SEE GRAPH"   (D-B)/(C-A)→M
Disp "AFTER YOU ARE","DONE,        "B+M(X-A)"→Y₈
  PRESS Y=.":Pause                 GraphStyle(0,5)
Func:FnOff :Plots Off              DispGraph
GridOn:                            Stop
- 9 . 4 → X m i n : 9 . 4 → X m a x    Lbl 3
1 → X s c l : 1 → Y s c l          " " → Y₈
```

Note 4A • BOWLING Program

The BOWLING program will plot ten points on a graph. Your goal is to find the fewest possible number of equations that hit all the points. The higher the level of difficulty, the larger the graph. There is a certain tolerance built in the program, so you don't have to hit the points exactly.

a. Run the program and choose your level of difficulty.

b. A graph appears with ten points. (Occasionally the program will plot duplicate points so you might see fewer than ten points.)

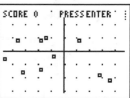

$[-5, 5, 1, -3, 3, 1]$

c. Press ENTER to trace on the points.

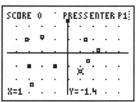

$[-5, 5, 1, -3, 3, 1]$

d. Enter an equation, trying to hit as many points as possible. When playing the "EASY" level, you'll score one point for the first point you hit, two points for the second point hit with the same line, four points for the third point hit, and so on. When playing the "MEDIUM" level, you'll score 3 points for the first point you hit, 12 points for the second point hit with the same line, 48 points for the third point hit, and so on. When playing the "HARD" level, you'll score 5 points for the first point you hit, 30 points for the second point hit with the same line, 180 points for the third point hit, and so on.

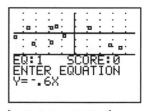

$[-5, 5, 1, -3, 3, 1]$

e. Continue tracing on points and entering equations until you have hit all the points.

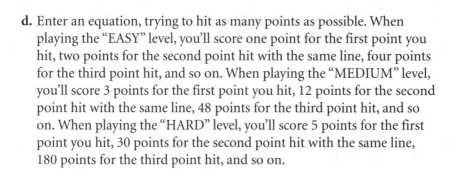

Clean-Up

If you quit the program before the end and don't use the QUIT option, you'll be left with a split screen. Press MODE and select Full. Then press 2nd [FORMAT] and select GridOff. You may also want to turn off the stat plot. Press 2nd [STAT PLOT] 4 (PlotsOff) ENTER, or press Y=, arrow to any plot that is highlighted, and press ENTER.

(continued)

```
PROGRAM:BOWLING
1→L:PlotsOff
FnOff :Full
ExprOff:Func
Menu("*** BOWLING ***","EASY",1,
   "MEDIUM",2,"DIFFICULT",3,"QUIT",Q)
Lbl 3:L+1→L
Lbl 2:L+1→L
Lbl 1:10→P
4.7L→H:-H→Xmin
H→Xmax:1→Xscl
3.1L→V:-V→Ymin
V→Ymax:1→Yscl
randInt(-23L,23L,P)/5→L₁
randInt(-12L,14L,P)/5→L₂
SortA(L₁,L₂)
Plot1(Scatter,L₁,L₂,□)
0→S:0L₁→L₃:0→N
Repeat P=0
0→T:N+1→N:Full
Text(0,0,"SCORE")
Text(0,24,S)
Text(0,44,"PRESS ENTER")
Pause
Lbl 8:Trace
L₁+L₃→L₁
SortA(L₁,L₂,L₃)
Horiz
Disp "EQ: SCORE: "
Output(1,4,N)
```

```
Output(1,14,S)
If N>1:Then
Disp "LAST Y="
Output(2,8,Str1)
End
Disp "ENTER EQUATION"
Input "Y=",Str1
String▶Equ(Str1,Y₁)
If Y₁=T:Goto 8
Full:DispGraph
For(J,1,P)
For(K,-.25,.25,.25)
L₁(J)+K→X
If Y₁≥L₂(J)-.3 and Y₁≤L₂(J)+.3
Then:T+1→T
For(A,L₁(J)-.4,L₁(J)+.4,.2)
For(B,L₂(J)-.4,L₂(J)+.4,.2)
Pt-Change(A,B)
End:End
100→L₃(J):.4→K
End:End:End
S+(2L)^T-1→S
P-T→P:End
Disp "FINAL SCORE",S
Disp "NUMBER OF"
Disp "EQUATIONS",N
PlotsOff
Lbl Q
Full:PlotsOff :GridOffExprOff
```

Note 4B · Using the DRAW Menu

To draw a vertical line, go to the Home screen and press [2nd] [DRAW] [4] (Vertical). Enter the *x*-coordinate of the vertical line you want to draw and press [ENTER]. If you want to draw vertical line(s) on the graph of an equation, it's best to draw the line(s) after you enter and graph the equation. To remove a vertical line, press [2nd] [DRAW] [1] (ClrDraw) [ENTER].

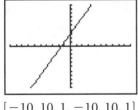

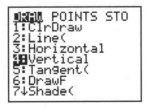

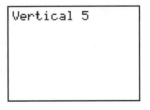

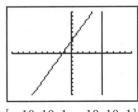

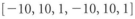

$[-10, 10, 1, -10, 10, 1]$　　　　　　　　　　　　　　　　　　　　　　　　　　　　$[-10, 10, 1, -10, 10, 1]$

Note 5A • Using Matrices to Solve Systems

This calculator has a built-in routine to convert a matrix into its equivalent solution form. Enter as MATRIX [A] the matrix that represents the system of equations you wish to solve. Note that this matrix must have one more column than its number of rows; for example, its dimensions might be 2×3, 3×4, or 7×8. In the Home screen, press 2nd [MATRIX], select [MATH], and select B:rref(. Then press 2nd [MATRIX] 1 ([A])) ENTER. (On the TI-83, press MATRX for the matrix menu.)

As an example consider the system $\begin{cases} 2x + y = 1 \\ 3x - 2y = 19 \end{cases}$

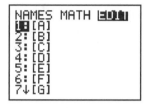 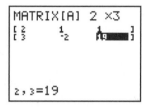  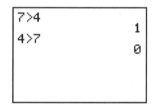

The solution to the system is $x = 3$ and $y = -5$.

Note 5B • Inequality Symbols

This calculator can test or evaluate an expression to determine whether it is true or false. This is called a Boolean test, after the mathematician Charles Boole. To find the equality and inequality symbols, press 2nd [TEST]. An expression is evaluated as 0 if it is false and as 1 if it is true.

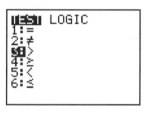 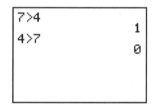

Note 5C • Graphing Inequalities in Two Variables

This calculator can graph an inequality in two variables by shading the screen above or below the graph of an equation. Enter an equation into the Y= screen. Then, in that same line, move the cursor as far left as it will go and press ENTER. Each time you press ENTER, the graph style changes and is indicated by the flashing cursor. To see the graph, press GRAPH.

To graph the inequality $y \geq -2 + x$, enter the equation for the line Y₁ $= -2 + x$ into the Y= screen. Then, move the cursor to the left of Y₁ and press ENTER ENTER to set the graph style to shade the portion of the screen above the line. Finally, press GRAPH.

 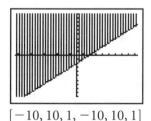

$[-10, 10, 1, -10, 10, 1]$

You can graph a system of inequalities by graphing two (or more) inequalities on the same screen.

To graph the system of inequalities $\begin{cases} y \geq -2 + x \\ y \leq 1 - x \end{cases}$

graph the first inequality as previously shown. Then, enter the equation for the line Y₂ $= 1 - x$ into the Y= screen. Move the cursor all the way to the left and press ENTER ENTER ENTER to set the graph style to shade the portion of the screen below the line. Finally, press GRAPH.

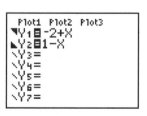 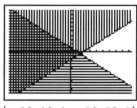

$[-10, 10, 1, -10, 10, 1]$

 ©2007 Key Curriculum Press

Note 5C/App • Graphing Inequalities Using the Inequalz App

An inequality graphing application is available for the TI-83 Plus and TI-84 Plus. It comes preloaded on the TI-84 Plus, and can be downloaded for the TI-83 Plus. Once you have the application on your calculator, follow these steps to use it.

Press [APPS], scroll down to :Inequalz, and press [ENTER]. Press any key to continue. Enter an expression and move onto the equals symbol. You'll see five choices, $=$, $<$, $\le$, $>$, and $\ge$, appear at the bottom of the screen. Press [ALPHA] then one of the five keys in the top row of your calculator to select the equality or inequality key you want. (For example, press [ALPHA] [F2] to choose $<$.)

Press [GRAPH] to graph the equation or inequality.

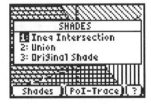

The Inequalz App is particularly useful if you want to graph the solution to a system of inequalities. For example, three inequalities are graphed here. It is not easy to identify the solution region.

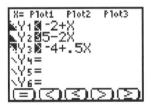
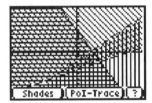

To shade only the solution region, press [ALPHA] [F1] to select Shades. Select 1:Ineq Intersection. Now only the solution region—the region where all three inequalities intersect—is shown.

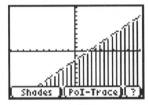
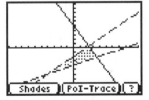

When finished graphing inequalities, quit the application by pressing [APPS], scrolling down to :Inequalz, pressing [ENTER], and selecting 2:Quit Inequal.

Note 6A • INOUTEXP Program

This program is similar to the INOUT program for linear rules. Here, however, the two lists are related by an exponential rule. You need to study the lists and determine the rule. The rule is in the form $A(1 + r)^x$, where x takes the values in the input list. Your job is to find the values for A and r. The program provides access to a "Calculator" screen as well as a "Hint" screen.

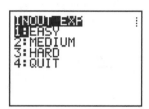
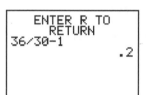
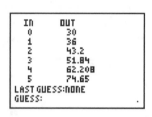

```
PROGRAM:INOUTEXP
Lbl 0:FnOff :PlotsOff
1→Xmin:2→Xmax
1→Ymin:2→Ymax
ClrDraw
"XXXXXXXXXXXXXXXXXXXXXXXXXXXXXXXXXX
  XXXXXXXXXXXXXXXXXXXXXX^XXXXXXX()/XXX
  XXX789*XXXXXX456-XXXXXX
  123+XXXXXX0.-X"→Str2
Text(0,20,"INOUT EXPONENTIAL")
Text(13,0,"THERE WILL BE TWO LISTS")
Text(20,0,"WITH AN EXPONENTIAL
  RULE.")
Text(27,0,"GUESSES SHOULD USE THE")
Text(34,0,"VARIABLE L₁ IN THE
  RULE,")
Text(41,0,"LIKE 20(1+.47)^L₁")
Text(55,20,"PRESS ENTER"):Pause
ClrDraw
Text(0,20,"INOUT EXPONENTIAL")
Text(13,0,"PRESS X FOR L₁")
Text(20,0,"PRESS Y= FOR THIS
  SCREEN")
Text(27,0,"PRESS WINDOW FOR HINT")
Text(34,0,"PRESS ZOOM FOR CALCULATOR
  MODE")
Text(41,0,"PRESS TRACE TO GIVE UP")
Text(55,20,"PRESS ENTER"):Pause
Menu("INOUT EXP","EASY",1,
  "MEDIUM",2,"HARD",3,"QUIT",Q)
```

```
Lbl 1
{0,1,2,3,4,5}→L₁
randInt(1,5)→A
10randInt(-5,5)→B
Goto 5
Lbl 2
seq(X,X,-3,8)→L₁
rand(12)→L₂
SortA(L₂,L₁)
6→dim(L₁)
SortA(L₁)
randInt(1,7)→A
5randInt(-10,10)→B
Goto 5
Lbl 3
seq(X,X,-9,9,.5)→L₁
rand(37)→L₂
SortA(L₂,L₁)
6→dim(L₁)
randInt(1,9)→A
randInt(-50,50)→B
Lbl 5
1+B/100→B
10A→A
A*B^L₁→L₂
List▶matr(L₁,L₂,[A])
"NONE"→Str4
ClrDraw
Text(0,0,"  IN      OUT")
For(J,1,6):For(K,1,2)
```
(continued)

(PROGRAM: INOUTEXP continued)

```
Text(7J,30K-20,round([A](J,K),3))
End:End
Repeat abs(sum(L₃-L₂))<.01 or K=14
Text(50,0,"LAST GUESS:"+Str4)
Text(57,0,"GUESS:          ")
"0+"→Str1
Repeat K=105 or K=14
Repeat K≠0
getKey→K:End
sub(Str2,K+1,1)→Str3
If K=11:Goto 8
If K=12:Goto 6
If K=13:Goto 9
Lbl 7
If Str3≠"X":Str1+Str3→Str1
If K=21 or K=32:Str1+"L₁"→Str1
length(Str1)→L
If K=24 and L>2:Then
L-1→L:sub(Str1,1,L)→Str1
End:If L>2:Then
Text(57,28,sub(Str1,3,L-2)+"  ")
Else:Text(57,28,"   ")
End:End:If L>2:Then
String▶Equ(Str1,r₁)
sub(Str1,3,L-2)→Str4
r₁+L₁-L₁→L₃
List▶matr(L₁,L₂,L₃,[A])
FnOff :ClrDraw
Text(0,0,"  IN  OUT  YOUR GUESS")
For(J,1,6):For(K,1,3)
Text(7J,7K²,round([A](J,K),3))
End:End:End:End
If K=14:Then
Text(57,0,"Ans:          ")
Text(57,16,A)
Text(57,24,"(1+")
Text(57,36,B-1)
```

```
Text(57,46+4(B<1),")^L₁")
Else
Text(50,10,"RIGHT!")
End:Pause
Goto 0
Lbl 6
ClrHome
Disp "A*(1+R)^L₁","","A WILL BE A
    MUL-","TIPLE OF 10 FROM","10 TO 90
    AND R","WILL BE BETWEEN","-0.99
    AND 0.99"
Pause :DispGraph
Goto 7
Lbl 8:ClrHome
Disp "PRESS..."
Disp "X    FOR L₁"
Disp "Y=   FOR HERE"
Disp "WINDOW FOR HINT"
Disp "ZOOM FOR CALC."
Disp "TRACE TO GIVE UP"
Output(8,3,"PRESS ENTER"):Pause
Goto 7
Lbl 9
ClrHome
Disp "ENTER R TO RETURN"
47→R
Repeat X=47
Input "",X
Disp X
End:DispGraph
Goto 7
Lbl Q
ClrHome
Disp "  PRESS ENTER","   TO
    REPLAY",""," PRESS"," 1 AND
    ENTER"," TO QUIT"
```

Note 6B • Equivalent Expressions

Two expressions are equivalent if they always have the same value regardless of the value of the variables. You can use your calculator to check whether two expressions are equivalent or not. The procedure is different depending on whether your expressions have one variable or more than one variable.

(continued)

Expressions with One Variable

To check whether or not $5 \cdot b \cdot b \cdot b$ is equivalent to $5b^3$:

a. Enter the expressions into Y₁ and Y₂ in the Y= screen, replacing the variable, in this case b, with x.

b. Press 2nd [TABLE] and look at the calculator table to see if both expressions give the same result for each value of x.

c. Press 2nd [TBLSET] and change TblStart and ΔTbl to make the table show any set of variable values you like.

This example shows that $5 \cdot b \cdot b \cdot b$ is equivalent to $5b^3$.

   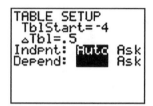

Expressions with More Than One Variable

Follow these steps to check whether or not $5a^4b^3 \cdot 3a^3b^5$ is equivalent to $15a^7b^8$:

a. Your calculator has a stored value for each variable a and b in its current memory. To see your variable values, enter a into the Home screen by pressing ALPHA [A] ENTER. Next, enter b into the Home screen and press ENTER. (The values in your calculator will probably be different than those shown on the screen here.)

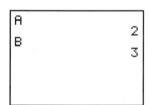

b. Compare the values of the two expressions. Enter each of the two expressions into the Home screen, pressing ENTER after each.

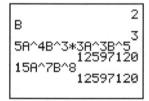

For the current variable values, the expressions are equal. But for the expressions to be equivalent, their values must be equal for any variable values. To be sure that the expressions are equivalent and not just equal for the one pair of variable values you tried, you need to evaluate the expressions for at least several other variable values. Note: If your expressions involve division by a variable, be sure not to use 0 as a variable value because you will get an ERR: DIVIDE BY 0 message. Division by 0 is undefined.

c. To change the currently stored value for a to -4, press (−) 4 STO▸ ALPHA [A] ENTER. Follow similar steps to change b. In the screen here, a has been changed to value -4 and b to value 2.5.

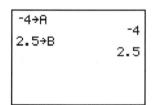

d. Again, enter both expressions into the Home screen, pressing ENTER after each to see if they have the same value.

e. Repeat **steps c** and **d** for other variable values.

This example shows that $5a^4b^3 \cdot 3a^3b^5$ is equivalent to $15a^7b^8$.

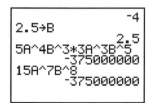

(continued)

Using Lists to Compare Expressions with More Than One Variable

Using list names as your variables allows you to check many variable values at the same time.

For example, follow these steps to check whether $\frac{12p^6q^8}{4p^2q^4}$ is equivalent to $3p^3q^2$:

a. Enter a sequence, of say three values, into list L1 (see **Note 1B**). Then enter a sequence of three values into list L2. The number of elements in each list must be the same. Do not use 0 in either list. Since this expression involves division by both variables, you will get an error message if either variable is 0.

b. Enter each expression into the Home screen, substituting list L1 for p and list L2 for q. Press ENTER after each expression. Compare the two sequences of expression values to see if they are the same.

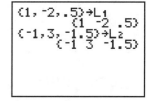

Even though the first expression value of each sequence is 3, the other two pairs of expression values do not match. Therefore, $\frac{12p^6q^4}{4p^2q^2}$ is not equivalent to $3p^3q^2$.

Note 6C • Scientific Notation

When your calculator is in normal mode (as it usually is), it displays some numbers in expanded notation and some numbers in scientific notation. Any number between 0.0001 ($1 \cdot 10^{-4}$) and 10,000,000,000 ($1 \cdot 10^{10}$) or between -0.0001 ($-1 \cdot 10^{-4}$) and $-10,000,000,000$ ($-1 \cdot 10^{10}$) is displayed in expanded form. A number greater than $1 \cdot 10^{10}$ or less than $-1 \cdot 10^{10}$ and a number within $1 \cdot 10^{-4}$ of zero is displayed in scientific notation. There is no way to set the calculator to display these numbers in expanded notation.

With your calculator in normal mode, any number can be entered in scientific notation form. To enter a number in scientific notation, locate the EE command above the comma key. Enter a number, press 2nd [EE], and then enter the power of ten.

To have your calculator display *all* numbers in standard scientific notation, press $\boxed{\text{MODE}}$, arrow to Sci, and press $\boxed{\text{ENTER}}$. Now any number, regardless of size or form, will appear in scientific notation.

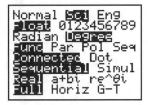

Note 6D • BOUNCE and PENDULUM Programs

Attach the motion sensor to the calculator and run either the BOUNCE or the PENDULUM program. The data will be collected in lists L1 and L2, and when the data collection is complete, a stat plot will be displayed on the calculator screen.

```
PROGRAM:BOUNCE
50→N
Disp "HOLD BALL 1 M OR","LESS FROM
   FLOOR.","HOLD PROBE 0.5 M","ABOVE
   THE BALL.","RELEASE BALL
   THE","SAME TIME YOU","PRESS
   TRIGGER."
Send({1,11,2,0,0,0})
Send({3,.06,N,1,0,0,0,0,1})
For(X,1,1000):End
Disp "PRESS ENTER","WHEN DONE."
Pause
Get(L₂)
Get(L₁)
max(L₂)-L₂→L₂
Plot1(Scatter,L₁,L₂,·)
FnOff :ZoomStat
```

```
PROGRAM:PENDULUM
31→N:ClrHome
Send({0})
Send({1,11,2,0,0,0})
Disp "GIVE CAN A SMALL","SWING,
   ALIGN THE","PROBE. PRESS","ENTER
   TO START"
ClrList L₂
Pause
Disp "COLLECTION WILL","TAKE 3
   MINUTES"
For(J,1,N)
Send({3,.04,99,0})
Get(L₁)
min(L₁)→L₂(J)
End
1-Var Stats L₂
Q₁-(Med-Q₁)²/(Q₃-2Med+Q₁)→K
K-L₂→L₂
seq(X,X,0,N-1)→L₁
Plot1(Scatter,L₁,L₂,·)
ZoomStat
```

You can also use the EasyData App to collect these data. See **Note 3B/App** for help.

Note 7A • Function Notation

Functions are entered into the Y= screen and are referred to by name as Y₁, Y₂, . . . , Y₉, Y₀.

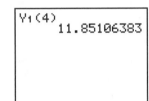

To evaluate a function for a particular *x*-value, for example, Y₁ when *x* = 4, as shown in the screen here, start in the Home screen and press [VARS], arrow to Y–VARS, select 1:Function..., and then select 1:Y₁. Then, press [(] [4] [)] [ENTER].

 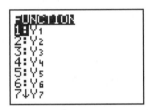 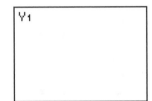

Note 7B • Some Functions

To use the command for squaring, enter a number in the Home screen and press [x²] [ENTER].

To use the command for square root, press [2nd] [√] in the Home screen. Then, enter a number, close the parentheses, and press [ENTER].

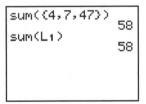

To use the command for the sum of a list, press [2nd] [LIST], arrow to MATH, and select 5:sum(. Then, press [2nd] [{] and enter the numbers of a list, separating each number with a comma. Close the braces and the parentheses, and press [ENTER].

Alternatively, press [STAT], select 1:Edit..., and then enter your numbers into a list, say list L₁. Then, enter sum(L₁) in the Home screen and press [ENTER].

 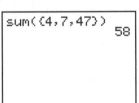 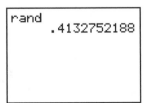

The command for a random number generates a random ten-digit decimal number between 0 and 1. Press [MATH], arrow to PRB, and select 1:rand. Then, press [ENTER].

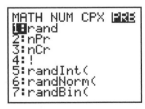

Note 7C • Absolute Value

To find the absolute value of a number, press MATH, arrow to NUMeric, and select 1:abs(. Then, enter a number, close the parentheses, and press ENTER.

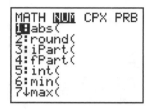

Note 7D • Friendly Windows

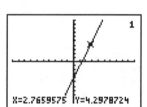

When you trace a function or locate a point on the screen, you often see long, "ugly" decimal values for the coordinates of your points. Sometimes, however, the values are "nice, friendly" values, like 2.4 or 4.84 or repeating decimals like 4.3333333.

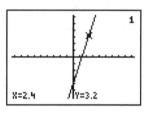

When the proper values are set for Xmin and Xmax in the WINDOW screen, the coordinate values of your points will be these "friendly" numbers for most functions. This is because the calculator screen is made of tiny square dots called pixels, and when you move horizontally across the screen, the x-coordinate changes by one pixel with each trace step. When the width of the domain, Xmax − Xmin, is cleanly divisible by 94, the window will be friendly. For example, if Xmin = 0 and Xmax = 94 or Xmin = 1 and Xmax = 10.4, the window will be friendly. (This is because the screen is 95 pixels across, not including the final column of pixels, which is not part of the graphing window.) In the first case, the x-coordinate changes by one unit with each trace step; in the second case, the x-coordinate changes by 0.1 unit with each trace step. (Note: The y-coordinate is calculated by evaluating the function for the x-coordinate. So, if the coefficients in a function are irrational, the y-coordinates will not be nice even in a friendly window.)

Two Friendly Square Windows

If you press ZOOM and select 4:ZDecimal you get a special type of small friendly window, called a friendly square window. It is friendly because it has the WINDOW values $[-4.7, 4.7, 1, -3.1, 3.1, 1]$. It is square because the horizontal and vertical scales in the screen are equal in size. In a square window, circles appear symmetric and round and the line $y = x$ makes a 45 degree angle with both axes. A square window is often the preferred window to use because it displays no visual distortion. However, this window, $[-4.7, 4.7, 1, -3.1, 3.1, 1]$, is sometimes too small to show much of the graph.

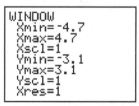
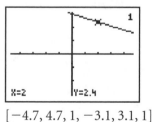

$$[-4.7, 4.7, 1, -3.1, 3.1, 1]$$

(continued)

   ©2007 Key Curriculum Press

To see more of the graph in the window, you can double the Xmin, Xmax, Ymin, and Ymax values $[-9.4, 9.4, 1, -6.2, 6.2, 1]$. This square window is referred to as the friendly window with a factor of 2.

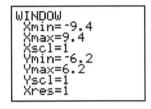   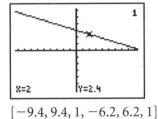

$$[-9.4, 9.4, 1, -6.2, 6.2, 1]$$

The friendly window with a factor of 2 is often a convenient window to use. To save it and recall it quickly, follow these steps.

    a. First enter the values $[-9.4, 9.4, 1, -6.2, 6.2, 1]$ into your WINDOW screen.

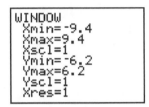

    b. Now, press ZOOM, arrow to MEMORY, and select 2:ZoomSto.

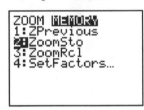

    c. The next time you need this window, say for the graph of $y = x^2$, press ZOOM, arrow to MEMORY, and select 3:ZoomRcl.

      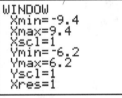   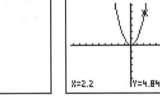

$$[-10, 10, 1, -10, 10, 1]$$ $$[-9.4, 9.4, 1, -6.2, 6.2, 1]$$

Other Friendly Square Windows

To assure that a window is square, the size of a horizontal step, called Δx, must equal the size of a vertical step, called Δy. The step size of the trace is Δx. In the square window $[-4.7, 4.7, 1, -3.1, 3.1, 1]$, Δx is 0.1. In the square window $[-9.4, 9.4, 1, -6.2, 6.2, 1]$, Δx is 0.2.

(continued)

Values for origin-centered friendly square windows are
$[-47 \cdot \Delta x, 47 \cdot \Delta x, 1, -31 \cdot \Delta y, 31 \cdot \Delta y, 1]$. For example, if Δx and Δy
equal 0.3, then . . .

 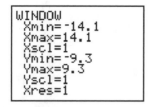 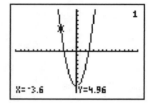

First-quadrant friendly square window values are $[0, 94 \cdot \Delta x, 1, 0, 62 \cdot \Delta y, 1]$.
Again, if Δx and Δy equal 0.3, then . . .

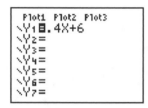 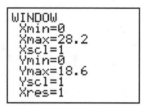 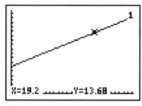

$[0, 28.2, 1, 0, 18.6, 1]$

Friendly Windows That Are Not Square

The Ymin and Ymax values of a friendly window can be changed to show a
larger or smaller range. The graph will look distorted and it will no longer be
square, but this might be necessary to see more of the graph. For example, the
graph of $y = x^2$ in the friendly square window $[-9.4, 9.4, 1, -6.2, 6.2, 1]$ runs
off the top of the graph for x-coordinates greater than 2.4. If you want to see
more of the graph, change the window to $[-9.4, 9.4, 1, -10, 100, 10]$. This is a
friendly window because the coordinates are still nice, but it is not square.

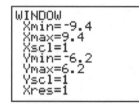 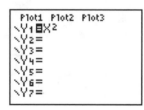 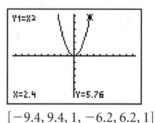

$[-9.4, 9.4, 1, -6.2, 6.2, 1]$

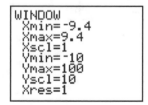 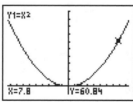

$[-9.4, 9.4, 1, -10, 100, 10]$

Note 8A • Animating a Figure

This is a sample program that translates the arrow in the project of Lesson 8.1. You can modify this program to translate a different figure or to involve other transformations.

Enter the following program into your calculator. (See **Note 0G** if you need help entering a program.)

```
PROGRAM:ANIMATE
{-7,-5,-6,-5,-5}→L₁
{-5,-3,-3,-3,-4}→L₂
Plot1(xyLine,L₁,L₂,.)
For(A,1,20)
L₁+0.6→L₁
L₂+0.35→L₂
DispGraph
End
```

Before you run the program, clear or disable any equations on the Y= screen and set the calculator to a friendly window with a factor of 2. (See **Note 7D** if you need help with friendly windows.) Also press [2nd] [FORMAT] and select AxesOff. Remember to turn the axes back on when you are finished with the program.

When you run the program, the arrow will appear to move from the lower left to the upper right of the screen in twenty frames.

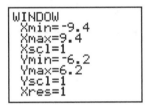

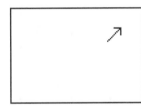

Note 8B • Transformations of Functions

Recall that your calculator uses Y1(x) as function notation. The function is defined by the expression you enter for Y1 in the Y= screen. You can use one function, say Y1(x), to define another function, say Y2(x). This allows you to do transformations. (See **Note 7A** to review selecting Y1 from the Y-VARS menu.)

For example, if Y1(x) = x², then the graph of Y2(x) = Y1(x + 4) is a translation of the graph of Y1(x) = x² to the left 4 units. This is the same as graphing Y2(x) = (x + 4)².

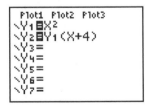
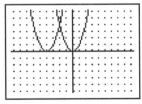

$[-9.4, 9.4, 1, -6.2, 6.2, 1]$

(continued)

The graph of $Y_2(x) = -3Y_1(x)$ is a reflection of the graph of $Y_1(x) = x^2$ across the x-axis and a vertical stretch by a factor of 3. This is the same as graphing $Y_2(x) = -3x^2$.

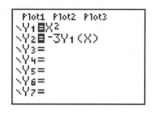
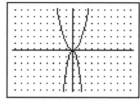

$[-9.4, 9.4, 1, -6.2, 6.2, 1]$

Note 8C • ABS Program

Enter the ABS program into your calculator or link it from another calculator. When you execute the program it will create a random absolute value graph on your screen. Study the graph in order to find its equation. If you want to know the coordinates of points on the function, press TRACE and the horizontal arrow keys. When you have a guess for the function, press Y=. Enter your guess and press either GRAPH or 2nd [TABLE] to compare your guess to the calculator's function, Y₀. If your guess needs adjustment, go back to Y= and make changes. When you have a match, the graphs of the two functions will coincide and their tables will be identical. Pressing TRACE and the arrow keys can help confirm or disprove the equivalence of the two graphs. When you have finished with a function, press 2nd [QUIT] and then press ENTER to replay or 1 ENTER to quit.

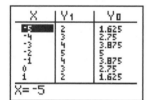
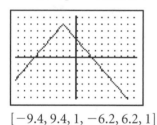
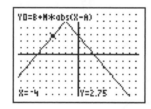
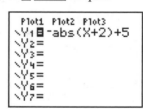
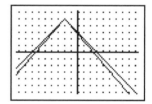

$[-9.4, 9.4, 1, -6.2, 6.2, 1]$

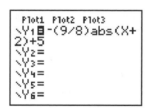
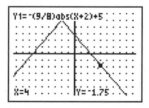

```
PROGRAM:ABS
ClrHome
Disp "  PRESS ENTER"," TO SEE
   GRAPH",""," AFTER YOU ARE","
   DONE","PRESS 2ND [QUIT]"
Pause
FnOff :PlotsOff
GridOn:
-9.4→Xmin:9.4→Xmax
1→Xscl:1→Yscl
-6.2→Ymin:6.2→Ymax
randInt(-9,8)→A
randInt(A+1,9)→C
```

```
ClrHome
Disp " PRESS ENTER","   TO
   REPLAY",""," PRESS"," 1 AND
   ENTER","   TO QUIT"
Lbl 1
randInt(-6,6)→B
randInt(-6,6)→D
If B=D:Goto 1
(D-B)/(C-A)→M
"B+M*abs(X-A)"→Y₀
GraphStyle(0,5)
DispGraph
```

Note 8D • PARAB Program

Enter the PARAB program into your calculator or link it from another calculator. When you execute the program it will create a random parabola on your screen. Study the graph in order to find its equation. If you want to know the coordinates of points on the function, press TRACE and the horizontal arrow keys. When you have a guess for the function, press Y=, enter your guess, and set the graph style to "line with trail" by moving to the left of Y1 and pressing ENTER four times. Press either GRAPH or 2nd [TABLE] to compare your guess to the calculator's function, Y0. If your guess needs adjustment, go back to Y= and make changes. When you have a match, the graphs of the two functions will coincide and their tables will be identical. Pressing TRACE and the arrow keys can help confirm or disprove the equivalence of the two graphs. When you have finished with a function, press 2nd [QUIT] and then press ENTER to replay or 1 ENTER to quit.

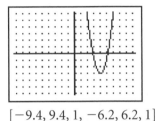

[−9.4, 9.4, 1, −6.2, 6.2, 1]

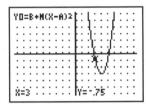

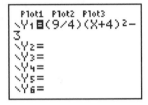

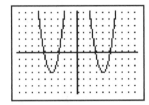

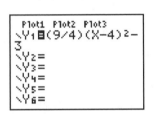

```
PROGRAM:PARAB
ClrHome
Disp " PRESS ENTER"," TO SEE
   GRAPH",""," AFTER YOU ARE","
   DONE","PRESS 2ND [QUIT]"
Pause
FnOff :PlotsOff
GridOn:
-9.4→Xmin:9.4→Xmax
1→Xscl:1→Yscl
-6.2→Ymin:6.2→Ymax
ClrHome
Disp " PRESS ENTER"," TO
   REPLAY",""," PRESS"," 1 AND
   ENTER"," TO QUIT"
```

```
randInt(-9,8)→A
randInt(A+1,9)→C
Lbl 1
randInt(-6,6)→B
randInt(-6,6)→D
If B=D:Goto 1
(D-B)/(C-A)²→M
"B+M(X-A)²"→Y₀
GraphStyle(0,5)
DispGraph
```

Note 9A/App • Collecting Jump and Roll Data Using the EasyData App

You must have a TI-83 Plus or TI-84 Plus to use this Note. If you have a TI-83, see **Note 9A** below. You can also use the programs CBRSET and CBRGET with any calculator. See page vi.

You will need a CBR (Calculator-Based Ranger).

Connect the CBR to the calculator. Press APPS and select EasyData. The CBR will immediately begin collecting distance data, which is displayed on your calculator screen.

Jump Option

To collect Jump data, press Setup (WINDOW) and select 2:Time Graph…. You will be shown the default settings for time interval and number of samples. Press Edit (ZOOM) to edit these settings. Enter 0.01 for the sample interval and press Next. Enter 100 for the number of samples and press Next. Then press OK.

Roll Option

To collect Roll data, press Setup (WINDOW) and select 2:Time Graph…. You will be shown the default settings for time interval and number of samples. Press Edit (ZOOM) to edit these settings. Enter 0.2 for the sample interval and press Next. Enter 50 for the number of samples and press Next. Then press OK.

Gathering Data

Press Start (ZOOM) to collect the data you have specified. You will be told that this function will overwrite the current list data. Press OK to continue. The calculator will collect the data and graph it.

To end the Application, press Main then press Quit. You will get a message telling you where the data is stored. Time data is in L_1, distance data is in L_6, velocity data is in L_7, and acceleration data is in L_8.

Note 9A • PARADAY Program

This program can be used with the TI-83, TI-83 Plus, and TI-84 Plus. However, if you have a TI-83 Plus or TI-84 Plus, you should consider using the EasyData App described in **Note 9A/App** above. You can also use the programs CBRSET and CBRGET with any calculator. See page vi.

This program reads either the CBL with a motion sensor or the CBR. Connect the CBL or CBR to your calculator.

Jump Option

Place the motion sensor on the floor pointing at a wall or object 1 meter away. Have the jumper stand halfway between. The jumper should jump after the sensor begins to "tick." Time and distance data will be graphed, and will be saved to L_1 and L_2, respectively.

Roll Option

Place the motion sensor on the high end of an inclined table. An empty 2 lb coffee can works well for this experiment. Starting at the low end of the table,

(continued)

roll the can gently up the table when the sensor begins to "tick." Time and distance data will be graphed, and will be saved to L_1 and L_2, respectively.

Get Data

When you are happy with the data you have gathered, you can link another calculator to the CBL or CBR and choose 3:GET DATA to retrieve the data into a second or third calculator. This will save you the difficulty of linking and sending lists among different models of calculators in the same group.

```
PROGRAM:PARADAY
Menu("PARABOLA
  DAY","JUMP",1,"ROLL",2,"GET
  DATA",3,"QUIT",5)
Lbl 1
Disp "PLACE CBR ON","FLOOR. STAND",
  "0.5M FROM CBR.","PRESS ENTER.",
  "JUMP WHEN YOU","HEAR THE CBR."
Pause
ClrHome
Send({1,0})
Send({1,11,3})
Send({3,0.01,100,0,0,0,0,0,1})
Goto 4

Lbl 2
Disp "PRESS ENTER WHEN","READY TO
  ROLL."
```

```
Pause
Send({1,0})
Send({1,11,3})
Send({3,0.2,50,0,0,0,0,0,1})
Goto 4
Lbl 3
Send({5,1})
Lbl 4
Get(L₂)
Get(L₁)
round(L₁,2)→L₁
Plot1(Scatter,L₁,L₂,·)
ZoomStat
Lbl 5
```

Errors

If you are not getting any data, check to see that the link cable is pushed in securely on both ends.

Note 9B • Cubes and Cube Roots

This calculator has two ways to find the cube and the cube root of a number. The first way involves functions found in the MATH menu. The second way uses the ∧ key.

To cube a number, enter the number in the Home screen, press MATH, select 3:³, and press ENTER. To find the cube root of a number, press MATH, select 4:³√(, enter the number, close the parentheses, and press ENTER.

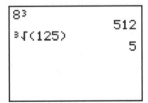

As an alternative, you can use the ∧ key. To cube a number, enter the number in the Home screen and then press ∧ 3 ENTER. To find the cube root of a number, enter the number in the Home screen and then press ∧ (1 ÷ 3) ENTER.

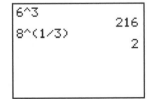

Note 10A • List of Random Integers

There are several ways to generate a list of random integers within an interval. Here we will use the randInt command. Press MATH, arrow to PRB, and select 5:randInt(to access the randInt command. Several examples will show you how this command works.

Integers From 1 through 100

The command randInt(1,100,4) will generate in the Home screen a sequence of four randomly generated integers from 1 through 100. To store the sequence into list L1, press STO→ and then 2nd [L1]. If you replace the 4 with 50, you will generate a sequence of 50 random integers.

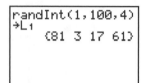

Two Possible Outcomes: Coin Toss/True-False Test

The command randInt(0,1,4) will generate a list of four 0's and 1's in random order. This command is useful for simulating a coin toss or perhaps randomly selecting answers on a true-false test.

```
randInt(0,1,4)
        {1 1 0 0}
```

Six Possible Outcomes: Tossing a Die

The command randInt(1,6,4) will generate a list of four random integers from 1 through 6.

```
randInt(1,6,4)
        {5 3 4 6}
```

Two Possible Outcomes: Random Walk

The command 2randInt (0,1,4)−1 will generate a list of four −1's and 1's. The screen here shows how this command works.

Viewing an Entry in a List

To avoid scrolling through a long list to see the last entry, enter 2nd [LISTNAME] (*n*), where *n* represents the number of the list entry you want to view in the Home screen. These two screens show how you can view the fortieth entry in the Home screen if there are 50 entries in the list.

(continued)

Errors

A list can only have 999 entries. If you get ERR:INVALID DIM, you may be trying to construct a sequence that is too long.

Note 10B • List Operations

(See **Note 1B** for instructions on entering a list.)

Sorting a List

When working with long lists, it is often more convenient to order the numbers rather than scanning the list for the first, last, middle, or any other value. Press STAT and you will see the command to sort in ascending order, SortA(, as well as the command to sort in descending order, SortD(. Select 2:SortA(and enter the list name. Close the parentheses and press ENTER.

For example, the command SortA(L1) will put list L1 in order from least to greatest.

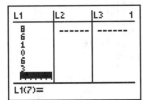 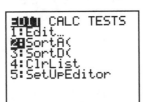 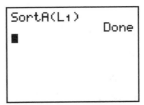 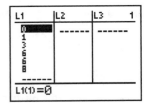

The command SortA(L2,L1) is very useful if you have two related lists and you want each entry in list L1 to stay with its corresponding entry in list L2. Notice that in the second list screen shown here, the entries in list L2 are in ascending order and the original pairings have not changed.

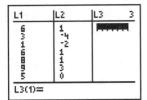 

Filling a List with a Sequence

To quickly fill a list with the sequence of integers from 1 through 50, you can use the sequence command seq(X,X,1,50,1). Press STAT 1 (Edit...), then arrow up and highlight a list name, in this case list L1. Press ENTER. Then press 2nd [LIST], arrow over to OPS, and select 5:seq(and complete the command. When you press ENTER and the list fills, the command at the bottom of the screen is replaced with the sequence.

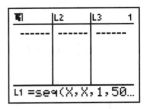

(continued)

Cumulative Sum of a List

The cumSum(command automatically calculates the cumulative sums of a list. If your list entries are in list L2, arrow over and highlight the list L3 name. Press [2nd] [LIST], arrow over to OPS, and select 6:cumSum(. Enter the name of the list for which you want to find the cumulative sums, in this case list L2, close the parentheses, and press [ENTER].

L1	L2	**L3**	3
1	1	------	
2	0		
3	0		
4	1		
5	1		
6	1		
7	0		

L3 =cumSum(L2)

L1	L2	L3	3
1	1	1	
2	0	1	
3	0	1	
4	1	2	
5	1	3	
6	1	4	
7	0	4	

L3(1)=1

Other List Functions

You can find the mean, median, sum, and other important numbers associated with a list by pressing [2nd] [LIST] and arrowing over to MATH. Always specify the list name and close the parentheses.

```
NAMES OPS MATH
1:min(
2:max(
3:mean(
4:median(
5:sum(
6:prod(
7↓stdDev(
```

1:min(the minimum value in a list

2:max(the maximum value in a list

3:mean(the mean of the list entries

4:median(the median of the list entries

5:sum(the sum of the list entries

Options 6, 7, and 8 are not used in this course.

Note 10C • Calculator Coin Toss

100 Trials

a. Enter the sequence of integers from 1 through 100 into list L1 on your calculator. This list will number the trials. (See **Note 10B.**)

b. Enter 100 randomly generated 0's and 1's into list L2. List L2 will represent the 100 coin tosses. Let 0 represent tails and 1 represent heads. (See **Note 10A.**)

c. Calculate and store the cumulative sums of list L2 into list L3. (See **Note 10B.**)

d. Calculate the ratio $\frac{L3}{L1}$ and store the results into list L4.

e. Make a scatter plot using list L1 as the x-values and list L4 as the y-values. Use the small dot as the mark. Define an appropriate graphing window for this scatter plot.

f. Enter the probability of tossing a head into Y1 in the Y= screen. Graph this equation along with the scatter plot.

(continued)

200 Trials

Enter the probability for your experiment into Y₁. To simulate the 200 trials, enter the commands below into the Home screen. After you have entered the commands, create a scatter plot of list L₁ versus list L₄ in a window of [0, 200, 20, 0, 1, .5]. You can access the ≤ symbol by pressing [2nd] [TEST] and choosing 6:≤.

seq(X,X,1,200) → L₁   Puts the numbers 1 through 200 in list L₁

rand(200) ≤ 1/2   Takes 200 random samples and compares them to the probability, $\frac{1}{2}$

cumSum(Ans) → L₃   Finds the cumulative sums of the number of successes in the 200 trials and stores them in list L₃

L₃/L₁ → L₄   Finds the ratios of the number of successes to the number of trials and puts them into list L₄

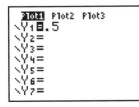
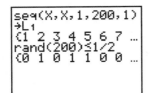
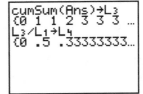
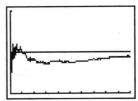

You can also enter the short program below so that you can rerun the simulation without re-entering the commands each time. (**See Note 0G.**)

```
Program:PROBSIM
seq(X,X,1,200)→L₁
rand(200)≤1/2→L₂
cumSum(L₂)→L₃
L₃/L₁→L₄
```

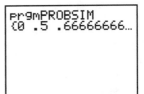

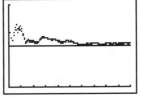

By making a small change in the PROBSIM program, you can adapt the program to work for an event that does not have outcomes of equal probability. In the third line, change the $\frac{1}{2}$ to a different probability value. You also need to enter the same probability value into Y₁.

Note 10D • Permutations

To find numbers of permutations use the nPr command. To find the nPr command, press [MATH], arrow over to PRB, and select 2:nPr. First enter the value of *n*, the number of objects. Then enter the nPr command, then enter the value of *r*, the number of objects chosen. Then press [ENTER].

(continued)

For example, to find the number of arrangements of 5 objects chosen 3 at a time, enter 5 nPr 3. The answer shows that there are 60 arrangements.

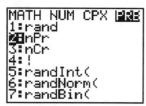
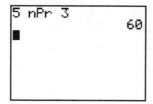

Note 10E • Combinations

To find numbers of combinations use the nCr command. To find the nCr command, press MATH, arrow over to PRB, and select 3:nCr. First enter the value of *n*, the number of objects. Then enter the nCr command, then enter the value of *r*, the number of objects chosen. Then press ENTER.

For example, to find the number of groupings of 5 objects chosen 3 at a time, enter 5 nCr 3. The answer shows that there are 10 different groupings.

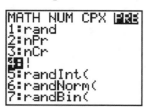
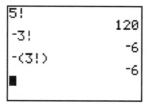

Note 10F • Factorial

To find the factorial command, press MATH, arrow over to PRB, and select 4:!. For example, to find 5!, press 5 MATH PRB 4:! ENTER.

In the order of operations, factorial has higher precedence than negation, so $-3!$ is equivalent to $-(3!)$.

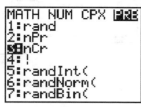
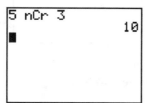

Note 10G • CITIES Program

The CITIES program will simulate random travel among six cities, stopping when a previously visited city is revisited.

Run the program and choose whether you'd like to view one, ten, or some other number of trips. If you choose 1: ONCE, you'll see travel among the six cities labeled A–F, and the histogram will show you the total number of cities visited on this trip. Press ENTER to simulate another trip or quit.

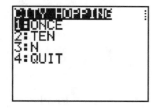
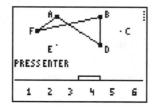

(continued)

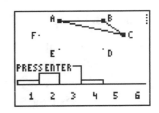

If you choose 2: TEN, you'll see ten trips simulated, and the histogram will show how many cities were visited during the ten trips. For example, the screen at right shows that three cities were visited during the tenth trip, and in the ten trips, one trip visited only one city, three trips visited two cities, five trips visited three cities, and one trip visited four cities.

If you choose 3: N, you can choose any number of trips. The program won't show each trip, but it will show a histogram with the number of trips that visited 1, 2, 3, 4, 5, and 6 cities. After you run this option, press 2nd [QUIT] ENTER to continue.

```
PROGRAM:CITIES                          randInt(1,6)→C
GridOff                                 K+1→K:
Lbl 0:1→N                               L₅(C)→L₃(K)
Menu("CITY HOPPING","ONCE",1,"TEN",     L₆(C)→L₄(K)
   2,"N",3,"QUIT",4)                    Line(L₃(K-1),L₄(K-1),L₃(K),L₄(K))
Lbl 2:10→N                              For(T,1,50):End
Lbl 1                                   End
ClrList L₁,L₃,L₄                        K-1→L₁(J)
Plot1(Histogram, L₁)
Plot2(xyLine, L₃, L₄,□)                 PlotsOn 1,2
PlotsOff                                DispGraph
Plot3(Scatter,L₅,L₆,·)                  Text(0,25,"A")
{3,5,6,5,3,2}→L₅:{18,18,14,10,10,14}→L₆ Text(0,67,"B")
1→Xmin:7→Xmax                           Text(12,11,"F")
1→Xscl:-5→Ymin                          Text(12,82,"C")
20→Ymax                                 Text(25,25,"E")
For(J,1,N)                              Text(25,67,"D")
{0,0,0,0,0,0}→L₂                        End:Text(35,0,"PRESS ENTER")
1→K                                     Text(55,9,"1   2   3   4   5   6")
ClrList L₃,L₄                           Pause
randInt(1,6)→C                          Goto 0
L₅(C)→L₃(K)                             Lbl 3
L₆(C)→L₄(K)                             PlotsOff 2,3
PlotsOff 2                              Prompt N
DispGraph                               ClrList L₁
Text(0,25,"A")                          Plot1(Histogram,L₁)
Text(0,67,"B")                          1→Xmin:7→Xmax
Text(12,11,"F")                         1→Xscl:0→Ymin
Text(12,82,"C")                         N/2→Ymax
Text(25,25,"E")                         For(J,1,N)
Text(25,67,"D")                         {0,0,0,0,0,0}→L₂
Repeat L₂(C)≠0                          0→K
1→L₂(C)                                 randInt(1,6)→C
Line(L₃(K)-.15,L₄(K)-.75,               Repeat L₂(C)≠0
   L₃(K)-.15,L₄(K)+.75)                 K+1→K:1→L₂(C)
Line(L₃(K)-.15,L₄(K)+.75,L₃(K)+.15,     randInt(1,6)→C
   L₄(K)+.75)                           End
Line(L₃(K)+.15,L₄(K)+.75,L₃(K)+.15,     K→L₁(J)
   L₄(K)-.75)                           DispGraph
Line(L₃(K)+.15,L₄(K)-.75,L₃(K)-.15,     End
   L₄(K)-.75)                           Lbl 4
```

Note 10H • Infinite Sums

To find the sum of terms of a recursive sequence, you can use a recursive routine. Rather than finding the *terms* of a recursive sequence, as you did in Chapters 0 and 3 (see **Notes 0D** and **3A**), here you'll find the *sum* of the terms of a recursive sequence.

For example, to find the sum of

$$1 + \frac{1}{2} + \frac{1}{4} + \frac{1}{8} + \frac{1}{16} + \cdots$$

you'll create the sequence 1, 1.5, 1.75, and so on. This sequence shows the sum of the first one term, the first two terms, the first three terms, and so on. You can look at what happens to this sequence as you add more terms of the sequence.

Begin by defining the initial values. The first term is 1, so enter {1, 1} and press ENTER. The first value is the index value, which tells you that you're looking at the first term, the sum of the first two terms, the sum of the first three terms, and so on. The second value tells you the sum. So {4, 1.875} indicates that the sum of the first four terms is 1.875.

To create the list of sums, write a formula that will generate the next line. The first value is Ans(1) + 1, meaning that each value will be 1 more than the previous value. The second value is the previous sum, Ans(2), plus the next term. In this case, each term is defined by $\left(\frac{1}{2}\right)^n$, where n is the previous term number, or Ans(1). So enter {Ans(1) + 1, Ans(2) + (1/2)^Ans(1)}. Press ENTER repeatedly until you see a pattern. The sum is approaching 2.

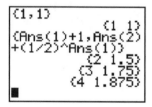
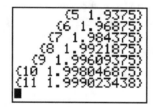

To find the sum

$$1 \cdot \left(\frac{1}{3}\right) + 2 \cdot \left(\frac{2}{3}\right)\left(\frac{1}{3}\right) + 3 \cdot \left(\frac{2}{3}\right)^2\left(\frac{1}{3}\right) + 4 \cdot \left(\frac{2}{3}\right)^3\left(\frac{1}{3}\right) + 5 \cdot \left(\frac{2}{3}\right)^4\left(\frac{1}{3}\right) + \cdots$$

start by entering the initial values. The first term is $\frac{1}{3}$, so enter {1, 1/3} and press ENTER. The next index value is given by Ans(1) + 1, and the sum of the next term is given by Ans(2) + (Ans(1) + 1)*(2/3)^Ans(1)*(1/3). The sequence of sums is shown. The sum is approaching 3.

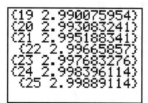
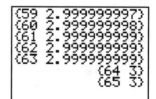

Note 11A • Square Windows

In a square window, the horizontal and vertical scales in the screen are equal in size. A square window is sometimes preferred because it displays no visual distortion.

See **Note 7D** to learn about friendly square windows. To create a window that is square, but not necessarily friendly, begin by entering a window range that shows what you want to see of the graph. Below, the square with vertices $(-6, -6)$, $(6, -6)$, $(6, 6)$, and $(-6, 6)$ is shown. Notice that it does not look like a square—it is distorted. You can see that the scales on the horizontal and vertical axes are not the same size.

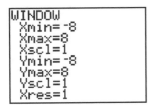

Now press ZOOM and select 5:ZSquare. The window is adjusted so that it is square. Notice that the square is no longer distorted.

 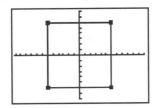 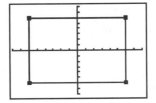

Note 11B • Trigonometric Functions

The trigonometric functions in this calculator work with angles that are measured either in degrees or in units called radians. In this course, all angles will be measured in degrees. Press MODE and check that your calculator is set to DEGREE mode.

The keys for the three trigonometric functions—sine, cosine, and tangent—are SIN, COS, and TAN. (If you look around you might find a calculator menu with sinh, cosh, and tanh. These are not the trigonometric functions you want to use.) Press the key with the function you need and enter an angle measure. Close the parentheses and press ENTER. The output is the trigonometric ratio expressed as a decimal number.

Note 11C • Inverse Trigonometric Functions

Press MODE and check that your calculator is set to Degree mode.

(continued)

To convert a trigonometric ratio back to an angle measure, use the inverse function found above the same key as the function. Press 2nd, select the inverse function, either [SIN⁻¹], [COS⁻¹], or [TAN⁻¹], and enter the ratio. Then, close the parentheses and press ENTER. The output is an angle measured in degrees.

```
sin(23)
         .3907311285
sin-1(.3907311285
)
              23
```

```
cos(63)
        .4539904997
cos-1(Ans)
               63
```

```
tan(47)
        1.07236871
tan-1(1.07236871)
               47
```

When using an inverse trigonometric function, the ratio can be entered either as a decimal number or as a fraction.

```
sin-1(1/2)
               30
cos-1(√(3)/2)
               30
tan-1(1/√(3))
               30
```

Often, when using an inverse trigonometric function, the degree measure of the output angle is not a whole number.

```
tan-1(4/3)
       53.13010235
cos-1(.3241)
       71.08894232
```

Key Curriculum Press
Innovators in Mathematics Education

Comment Form

Please take a moment to provide us with feedback about this book. We are eager to read any comments or suggestions you may have. Once you've filled out this form, simply fold it along the dotted lines and drop it in the mail. We'll pay the postage. Thank you!

Your Name _____

School _____

School Address _____

City/State/Zip _____

Phone _____ Email _____

Book Title _____

Please list any comments you have about this book.

_____
_____
_____
_____
_____
_____
_____
_____
_____
_____
_____

Do you have any suggestions for improving the student or teacher material?

_____
_____
_____
_____
_____
_____
_____

To request a catalog, or place an order, call us toll free at 800-995-MATH, or send a fax to 800-541-2242. For more information, visit Key's website at www.keypress.com.

Fold carefully along this line.

NO POSTAGE
NECESSARY
IF MAILED
IN THE
UNITED STATES

BUSINESS REPLY MAIL
FIRST CLASS   PERMIT NO. 338   EMERYVILLE, CA

POSTAGE WILL BE PAID BY ADDRESSEE

Key Curriculum Press
Innovators in Mathematics Education

Attn: Editorial Department
1150 65th Street
Emeryville, CA 94608-9740

Fold carefully along this line.

Comment Form

Please take a moment to provide us with feedback about this book. We are eager to read any comments or suggestions you may have. Once you've filled out this form, simply fold it along the dotted lines and drop it in the mail. We'll pay the postage. Thank you!

Your Name _____

School _____

School Address _____

City/State/Zip _____

Phone _____ Email _____

Book Title _____

Please list any comments you have about this book.

_____
_____
_____
_____
_____
_____
_____
_____
_____
_____

Do you have any suggestions for improving the student or teacher material?

_____
_____
_____
_____
_____
_____
_____

To request a catalog, or place an order, call us toll free at 800-995-MATH, or send a fax to 800-541-2242.
For more information, visit Key's website at www.keypress.com.

Fold carefully along this line.

NO POSTAGE
NECESSARY
IF MAILED
IN THE
UNITED STATES

BUSINESS REPLY MAIL
FIRST CLASS   PERMIT NO. 338   EMERYVILLE, CA

POSTAGE WILL BE PAID BY ADDRESSEE

Key Curriculum Press
Innovators in Mathematics Education

Attn: Editorial Department
1150 65th Street
Emeryville, CA 94608-9740

Fold carefully along this line.